CW01082203

INNOVATION
THE SWEDISH WAY

This book has been produced
in cooperation with the
Royal Swedish Academy of Engineering Sciences
with support from

ERICSSON SAAB SEB STORAENSO

INNOVATION
THE SWEDISH WAY

Henrik Berggren   Eva Krutmeijer

MAX STRÖM

Contents

Preface by HM The King of Sweden

Only a few years ago, I had the pleasure of welcoming Sweden's ten millionth resident into the world.

There are a few more of us now. But our population is still relatively small. In geographical terms, we are on the periphery of Europe.

Nevertheless, Sweden is a leader when it comes to research and development. Our country consistently ranks as the most innovative in the EU. No other nation in the world has generated as many revolutionary innovations or as many patents per capita as Sweden.

One contributing factor has been our strong tradition of innovative thinking and entrepreneurship, maintained over centuries by brilliant Swedish engineers, inventors and businesspeople.

Reading this book, one realises that trust and cooperation also seem to promote innovation. A desire and willingness to work together with others has helped make Sweden successful.

As a Swede, I feel gratitude and pride in all the pioneers from previous generations who believed in their ideas and refused to give up. With their curiosity, energy and talent, they are role models for us all.

It is my hope that this book will inspire even more people to think creatively and continue to be open to new ideas. I look forward to many more Swedish innovations emerging in the next few years and contributing to a better future – for Sweden, Europe and the world.

Doing something no one has ever done before

By most measures, Sweden is an unusually innovative country. Not only has this small economy in Europe's far north claimed the first position in the European Commission's innovation rankings every year, Sweden also ranks in the top three in the Global Innovation Index. This ranking is based on parameters such as degree of knowledge and technology outputs, infrastructure and human capital. With a population of a little over 10 million, Sweden also performs remarkably highly in terms of innovation start-ups.

Sweden's position as an innovation powerhouse has long been credited to its tradition of higher education. In the early 20th century, Sweden's national character was said to be shaped by 'an inclination towards mechanical studies and a predilection for producing technical innovations'. But even with a long list of impressive names like John Ericsson and Alfred Nobel: how has Sweden managed to produce so many successful engineers and inventors? Is there something in Sweden's history or culture that has spurred so many innovations?

There are several factors contributing to this spirit of ingenuity.

Literacy
Sweden's high literacy rate has been a key element in the country's tradition of innovation. Even in the mid-18th century, between 70 and 90 per cent of Swedes could read. Because of the country's small population, books and other printed materials intended for a wide audience had to focus on popular topics like farming and handicrafts. Voltaire did not have many readers in Sweden, but the Swedish farmer's almanac certainly did.

Stability and meritocracy
The stability of the Swedish state has also played a crucial role. Sweden became an independent nation in 1523, with a legal administrative framework set up in the 17th century. That enabled the rise of a meritocratic society, where talent, education and achievement were more important than family connections or wealth. There are many examples of innovators who rose from modest circumstances to leading positions in major industries by virtue of their abilities and creativity.

Property rights

Feudalism was not as deeply entrenched in Sweden as elsewhere in Europe. Although many farm labourers were locked into tenancy contracts that required them to pay fees, large landowners in Sweden never acquired the same degree of power as in other countries.

The establishment of the land survey authority in the 17th century helped to define property rights. With secure land tenure, farmers could invest in new farming techniques and other improvements. Intellectual property rights were also introduced early on. Sweden was not the first European country to issue patents, but with high levels of literacy in the population, even farmers' sons could obtain patents to protect their intellectual property rights in their inventions.

International influences

Openness to the world has also been an important factor. Though the French philosopher René Descartes tragically succumbed to Stockholm's cold weather on a visit to the city at the invitation of Queen Christina in the 17th century, that was an early example of Swedish willingness to look abroad for new ideas. People in small, peripheral countries often recognise the importance of going beyond their own borders for inspiration. For centuries, Sweden has measured itself against the prevailing power of the era, whether that was France, Britain, Germany or the United States. Swedish innovators have been inspired by ideas and inventions originating in other countries. There are also examples of innovators who came here from other countries and found fertile ground for their creativity. Diversity has clearly been a significant element in Sweden's innovation culture.

Political reforms

Sweden was a late adopter of industrialisation and modernisation, due in no small part to the country's inability to let go of its imperialist dreams of reinstating the Swedish Empire. But when policymakers realised that the nation's future had to be built within its borders, progress was swift. Comprehensive political reforms implemented from the mid-19th century onwards – including compulsory schooling, expansion of the railway infrastructure, abolition of privileged monopolies in the guild system, opportunities to invest while limiting one's risk (banks and limited-liability companies with share ownership) and increased openness and free trade – laid the foundations for the next century's strong economic progress driven by innovation.

Natural resources

The importance of Sweden's natural resources cannot be overestimated. Forests provided fuel and building materials, ore deposits provided iron and rivers generated power. These natural resources also spurred inventiveness – each improvement resulted in many follow-on benefits. And there were profits to be made: Swedish granite, steel and timber had buyers all over the world.

Sweden's lack of other natural resources also spurred innovations. The absence of fossil fuel reserves led to the development of alternative energy sources and energy-efficient technologies.

Open society

Universal voting rights were enacted in Sweden in 1921, which was relatively late, but a strong democratic tradition had already been in place via citizens' organisations such as temperance movements, the Lutheran Church, trade unions, sports clubs and adult study groups. Members enjoyed equal rights and made decisions by democratic means, which created trust in a non-hierarchical setting. It engendered a culture in which status was less important than competence and relevant knowledge.

Sweden became a more open society that was receptive to new ideas from all quarters. The country's tradition of popular movements was reinforced by employment security. In Sweden, employees cannot be fired for making a mistake or submitting unsolicited suggestions. That has led to a culture of openness and trust and, combined with Swedish companies' typically flat organisational structure, has created fertile ground for innovation.

Collaboration

Sweden's severe climate has also made people more willing to work together. People living in vast forests and remote fells had little chance of making it through tough winters if they didn't have good relations with their neighbours. People helped each other to build houses and barns and provided hospitality to travellers. It was impossible to survive without collaboration.

Of course, Sweden has not been entirely free of social and political conflict, but difficulties have usually been solved through compromise and consensus. Respect for skills and knowledge, trust in public authorities and a desire to find shared solutions have created a climate of innovation. Many of the innovations presented in this book are the result of collaboration between several individuals, between companies and also between industries and academic spheres. This interest in collaboration has generated an ability to create synergies in innovation and research.

Some of Sweden's most economically significant engineering innovations have been the result of long-term collaborations between a handful of companies, such as Ericsson and ASEA/ABB, working with public-sector bodies in sectors including telecoms, power generation and rail transport. Such joint projects have produced mobile telephones and digital exchanges, revolutionary high-voltage technology and the X2000 tilting train.

In the medical field, universities, businesses and hospitals have collaborated to yield tangible results. Hässle, a pharmaceutical firm that was acquired by Astra in the 1940s, is an example where the intersection of basic research, applied studies and clinical trials led to the development of omeprazole (Losec), a commercially successful ulcer medication. Astra Zeneca and other pharmaceutical companies continue to see the benefits of maintaining close links with academia and health care.

In the Cold War years, Sweden chose to remain neutral and invested vast resources into research and development to build up a strong national defence. Saab and the Swedish armed forces worked together closely to design and produce a number of fighter aircraft, from the Tunnan in the 1940s to the Gripen, still in production.

Free education

Sweden's school system has also played a crucial role. Nearly half of all Swedes have some post-secondary education, and over a third have a college or university degree. All state education in Sweden is free of charge, even at university level. College and university students also receive a small grant and can take out a student loan from the state at low interest rates. They do not need to repay the loan until they start working. So students' talent and ability are what count, not their parents' finances. Studies are something that students choose for themselves, not something their parents decide for them.

Schools emphasise entrepreneurship, and many young Swedes are able start their own small businesses when they are still in school. Studies show that students who start businesses in school often go on to launch companies later on – and they enjoy higher incomes and lower unemployment than other groups.

Research

Investment in research and development represents 3.5 per cent of Sweden's GDP. That is high in international terms. Around 70 per cent of that investment comes from the private sector. It is hardly surprising, then, that companies' R&D divisions are the largest source of Swedish innovations, accounting for around half. A fifth of the country's innovations originate with university-based researchers, and around a third come from independent creative individuals. Both Skype and Spotify fall under that third category.

Swedish universities have a custom known as 'professor's privilege', in which scientists and researchers retain ownership of their ideas and research results – a not inconsiderable but often debated incentive. It means that academics will typically have a stake in the companies that develop and refine their innovation, unlike in many other countries, where the rights in discoveries and inventions are retained by the institution where they came about.

Today, climate, energy and environmental challenges are motivating a transformation of Sweden's industrial base. Swedish industry can enjoy a competitive advantage from being ahead of the game as the world moves away from fossil fuels. Small start-ups play a major role, but there are also large-scale joint projects involving universities, businesses and public authorities. Funding for scientific research is now prioritising climate and the environment.

Communications infrastructure

Covering a long distance from north to south, Sweden has always been an early adopter of new modes of communication. It had the most telephones per capita at the end of the 19th century. A century later, internet use was already well established. A Swedish prime minister was the first world leader to email the US president in 1994. Broadband services were rolled out quickly, and by 2010, 92 per cent of Swedes were connected to the internet. The Swedish government also provided grants for households to acquire personal computers. Soon, the 'folkhemmet', or 'people's home' as Sweden is sometimes called, was online. Work on mobile broadband – a Swedish innovation – was underway even before the internet was in widespread use.

Access to capital

Sweden is a small country. It's also a 'flat' country in terms of hierarchies, with short distances between people working in any particular field. It benefits from a diverse range of investors, which contributes to a strong innovation culture. An innovator who is turned down by one investment fund or venture capital firm can turn to an investor with a different profile for a better match. That principle applies to investments via public-sector bodies as well as the full range of large and small private-sector investors. One innovation that demonstrates the principle in practice is pyrosequencing, which revolutionised the process of DNA analysis. When no other source of funding was available to the scientists, the venture capital firm HealthCap realised the technology could play a crucial role in diagnosing illness, making Sweden a suitable base for establishing a tech business.

Money is not everything. It also takes imagination – the ability to envisage and persuade others how an innovation will work in a future that is still to come. Another way to measure this: Stockholm has the highest number of 'unicorns' – privately held start-ups valued at over US$1 billion – per capita after California's Silicon Valley.

This book tells the stories of 50 innovations that helped to transform Sweden from one of the world's poorest countries to one of the wealthiest. From Celsius to Spotify, we focus on the people behind the ideas, the circumstances they lived in and the forces that inspired them. Sweden has a long history, but that legacy clearly doesn't hold Swedes back when it comes to adopting new ideas and questioning old ways.

We have adopted a broad definition of 'innovation' and chosen to include political and social concepts that arose in Sweden and later spread to other countries. We have chosen to showcase everything from practical innovations that make everyday life easier to revolutionary technical and medical developments that have changed the world. The common denominator is that they are all new things that have had a beneficial effect. Innovations are distinguished from inventions or discoveries in that an innovation solves a problem that people, companies or governments are prepared to pay for. An innovation has to be disseminated, find a market or create value in a broad context.

Naturally, these successes have emerged from all sorts of circumstances. Up to the end of the 19th century, innovators were usually individuals who managed to see their inventions travel around the world. In the 20th century, large corporations had a hand in many innovations and then continued to improve and refine them. Sweden's engineering tradition delivered the goods. Since the 1990s, society has once again been characterised by a more disruptive, entrepreneurial climate, supported by the range and scaleability of digitalisation, where individual innovations can rapidly transform an entire market.

Choosing which innovations to include from Sweden's vast inventory has been a difficult task. The selections presented in this book reflect our personal preferences. We have chosen to focus on the innovative spirit behind each story. We hope this book will inspire you as much as the research and writing process has enlightened us.

Henrik Berggren, Eva Krutmeijer and Jeppe Wikström

From zero to a hundred

THE CELSIUS TEMPERATURE SCALE

Some innovations come about when the right person is in the right place. The Celsius temperature scale probably wouldn't have seen the light of day in a land without a natural supply of snow and ice. Today, in nearly every country around the world, it's obvious to think about the freezing point of water as zero, and everything below that as a negative number. In the early 18th century, though, over 30 different temperature scales were in use. It took Anders Celsius from Sweden in northern Europe to introduce the centigrade temperature scale, which quickly became the dominant model. Today it is the generally accepted scale used for measuring temperature.

One temperature system that many people used in Celsius' time – and which is still in use in the United States and a few other places – is the Fahrenheit scale. It was developed in 1724, based on the lowest and highest temperatures occurring in Daniel Gabriel Fahrenheit's homelands of northern Germany and the Netherlands. To calibrate the scale, Fahrenheit assigned the value of zero to the lowest temperature he could achieve. To do this, he mixed ice water with salt. The temperature he registered was equivalent to –18 degrees Celsius. He chose normal human body temperature as his other reference point and assigned it the value of 96 degrees Fahrenheit. He divided the scale between those two points into 12 increments, then further subdivided each increment into eight degrees, giving a total of 96 degrees. Very complicated. And far from exact – not least of all because body temperature varies from person to person.

Anders Celsius, a young Swedish astronomer, would change all that. At the tender age of 29, he had been appointed Professor of Astronomy at Uppsala University. As a discipline, astronomy was closely allied to mathematics, and Celsius lectured in both subjects. His father and both of his grandfathers were astronomers, and Anders displayed a particular talent for mathematics early on. By the age of 12, he had solved every problem in a university-level maths textbook.

Celsius made copious observations of celestial bodies, and he was obsessed with the Northern Lights. During a lengthy research tour in continental Europe, he published a paper whose Latin title translates as '316 Observations of the Aurora Borealis, 1716–1732'. That study

This thermometer was created by Anders Celsius. He used it to conduct the experiments that led to the temperature scale we know today, in which water freezes at 0 degrees and boils at 100 degrees. The scale originally ran in the opposite direction, with the boiling point at 0.

attracted a great deal of attention, and young Celsius soon became acquainted with eminent astronomers of the day, including Cassini and Halley, as well as makers of some of the finest scientific instruments.

Astronomical instruments were an entire discipline in those days. Skilled makers – many of whom were astronomers themselves – built clocks and telescopes, quadrants and other devices for measuring angles. Anders Celsius placed orders for some high-quality tools to equip the astronomical observatory he commissioned in Uppsala in 1741 – the first in Sweden.

Sir Isaac Newton's theories were a topic of intense debate within universities and scientific academies at that time. Was it really possible that the same force that caused an apple to fall from a tree also affected the movement of the planets in the heavens?

A discussion on the merits of Newton's laws of motion was held at the Académie des Sciences in Paris when Celsius happened to be in the city. The academy members were particularly fascinated by Newton's theory of rotation and centrifugal force. If the theory was correct, a French scientist by the name of Maupertuis and his supporters argued, then wouldn't the Earth's rotation around its axis mean our planet was not perfectly spherical but rather slightly bulged at the equator and compressed at the poles? Celsius soon got caught up in a lively debate, and before long, a plan for a large-scale experiment started to take shape. By measuring the angle to a star against a north–south baseline on the ground, it should be possible to determine the length of one degree of a meridian arc. If the arc was longer at the poles than at the equator, that would prove that the Earth actually is somewhat flattened at the poles – supporting Newton's theory.

Maupertuis proposed an ambitious experiment to find the answer. Presumably it was Anders Celsius who suggested Sweden's northern Tornedalen region, located on the Arctic Circle, as a suitable place to take measurements. For the measurements at the equator, a site in present-day Ecuador was chosen.

Maupertuis himself led the northward expedition, accompanied by five French scientists and two Swedes. It was an opportunity for Celsius to perform a large number of measurements at the Arctic

Anders Celsius began keeping one of the world's first temperature records in 1722. Changes in climate conditions in the past 50 years are clearly noticeable, with higher temperatures and fewer cold winters.

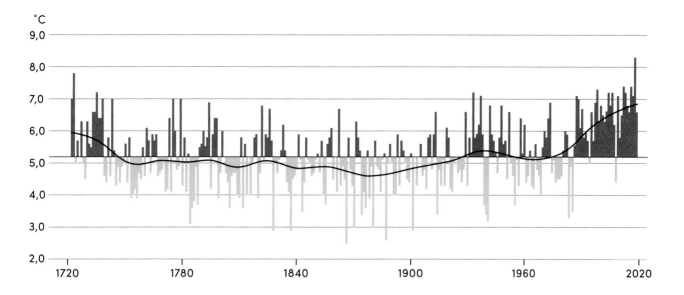

Circle in the autumn and winter of 1736–1737. Afterwards, the scientists were delighted to learn that the results obtained did indeed confirm Newton's theory. Upon his return to Paris, Maupertuis was hailed as a hero. Voltaire said he had managed to 'flatten the Earth, as well as Cassini'.

When Anders Celsius returned home to Uppsala in the autumn of 1737, he resumed the series of experiments with temperature readings he had started in 1722. The thermometer he used consisted of a small amount of mercury sealed inside a narrow glass tube. As the liquid mercury warms up, it expands more than the glass, so the level of the mercury rises. Celsius was very precise in his measurements. He realised that changes in atmospheric pressure affected his results, so he took care to take temperature measurements in different places so he could construct a scale that would work everywhere. The simplest method was to gather snow and ice to take the minimum reading and to boil water for the maximum. The simplest method is often the best.

In 1742, Celsius unveiled a temperature scale in which the boiling point of water at normal air pressure served as one reference point, with the freezing point of water as the other. Celsius set the boiling point at 0 and the freezing point at 100 at normal air temperature. He divided the distance between those two points into 100 degrees (the source of the term *centigrade*). Not long after that, a French scientist named Jean-Pierre Christin reversed the scale to make 0 the freezing point and 100 the boiling point – though many patriotic Swedes prefer to attribute that change to their very own Carl von Linné, known abroad as Linnaeus. Celsius was quick to adopt the updated version, and so the temperature scale took on its present form. The Celsius scale went on to conquer the world, and today it is as firmly established as the thermometer itself.

The queen of alcohol
MAKING POTATOES INTO AQUAVIT

When Eva Ekeblad De la Gardie became the first woman to be elected to the Royal Swedish Academy of Sciences in 1748, one might imagine that the assembled gentlemen were overjoyed. Ekeblad had hit upon the brilliant idea to distil potatoes into liquor. Perhaps the other members of the Academy noticed the potential for Swedish distilleries and for the Academy's own future celebrations. Swedish aquavit is known around the world – though perhaps not for being the healthiest innovation. Nevertheless, it has an interesting history.

Eva De la Gardie was born in Stockholm on 10 July 1724, the 10th of 14 children in her family, though all but two of her older siblings died in early childhood. Eva had the good fortune to be born into a wealthy, aristocratic family. Her father, Magnus Julius De la Gardie, was a councillor of the realm, a marshal of the Swedish army and a count. Her mother, Hedvig Catharina Lillie, was passionate about social issues and hosted political salons in the family's home.

At the age of 16, Eva married Claes Ekeblad, a count who was active in politics. He owned a house in central Stockholm – located on the site of today's Royal Opera House – as well as a large estate in Västergötland in southern Sweden.

Eva De la Gardie was described as a 'capable, talented and temperamental woman who inspired respect'. She gave birth to eight children, all but one of whom survived to adulthood. In addition to managing her family's city and country households, Eva soon developed an interest in science. The practical experiments she conducted would eventually earn her a place in history.

In 1655, Olaus Rudbeck had planted some potatoes in Uppsala's Botanical Gardens, but he was not particularly interested in the tubers under the soil. The man most often cited in connection with the potato's introduction in Sweden is Jonas Alströmer, a prominent industrialist and farmer with many strings to his bow. Notably, he was one of five men who met at the House of Nobility in Stockholm on 4 June 1739 to establish the Royal Swedish Academy of Sciences. Alströmer was allocated Seat Number 1 in the Academy. He does have some relevance for this story, though it is doubtful whether he really was the driving force behind the popularisation of the potato in Sweden, as every Swedish schoolchild is taught. Instead, Swedish soldiers might have learned to eat potatoes while fighting in the Pomeranian War in northern Germany and then brought that habit back with them in the 1760s – home to a country whose impoverished population was used to living on a diet of turnips and rutabagas (known as *swede* in the UK).

Eva De la Gardie, on the other hand, played a major role in popularising the potato in Sweden. The efforts of this upper-class lady proved to be of great benefit, particularly in combating hunger. For example, she showed how to make bread ingredients go further by adding boiled, mashed potatoes to the dough. She also turned her scientific mind to other uses for the humble potato. Before long, she had figured out how to produce potato flour – a pure starch. She also made a potato-based powder for use on the extravagant wigs that were in fashion at the time. Perhaps not as beneficial to the population as potato starch, but still important to the upper-class people who wore them. It meant they could switch from using powders which contained toxic arsenic.

Eva Ekeblad De la Gardie created a number of innovations. Many people appreciated her efforts to distil aquavit from potatoes.

But Eva De la Gardie is best known for developing potato-based aquavit. Previously, distilled spirits had been made from grain such as wheat, rye or barley. Her distillation method based on potatoes meant that more grain was available for Swedes' bread and porridge.

After Jonas Alströmer, Anders Celsius, Carl von Linné (Linnaeus) and other eminent members of the Royal Swedish Academy of Sciences elected Eva De la Gardie to join their ranks in 1748, the Academy's records from 12 November of that year include an essay entitled 'Experiments to produce bread, aquavit, starch and powder from potatoes, performed by Eva De la Gardie'. The article does not reveal a full account of her procedures, but in purely chemical terms, she would have had to come up with a more complex technique than the typical processes used with grain. In those days, people were unaware that the potato's cell walls had to be broken down to release the starch, and that the potato – unlike cereal crops – contains minimal amounts of the enzyme that converts starch into glucose, the simplest sugar molecule.

In photosynthesis, plants take in carbon dioxide from the air and water from the ground, as well as energy from the sun. They generate oxygen and sugar molecules, which are the building blocks of plant cells. Fermentation occurs when this reaction plays out in reverse, in the absence of oxygen, producing ethanol rather than carbon dioxide and water. It is similar to the reaction that occurs when our muscles produce lactic acid during hard exertion due to a lack of oxygen. Thus, an oxygen-free environment is needed for yeast to produce ethanol.

After fermentation, the next step is distillation, which increases the liquid's alcohol concentration. Distillation is a heating process that takes advantage of the different boiling points of water and alcohol. In the 18th century, distillation was done over an open fire, so people said they were 'burning' the spirits. As a result, distilled spirits are called *brännvin* in Swedish. The English word 'brandy' shares this origin.

When Eva De la Gardie died at the age of 61, she had been widowed for 15 years. It would take nearly 200 years until the next woman was elected to the Royal Swedish Academy of Sciences, the body that chooses the recipients of the Nobel Prizes in chemistry and physics each year.

Potatoes being pressed to make aquavit. The photo was taken in 1923 at Grimstorp, Småland in southern Sweden.

Warmth that lasts

SWEDISH TILED STOVE

Sweden was hit by an energy crisis in the 18th century. The nation's forests, which supplied timber for building as well as fuel, could not keep up with demand. Inefficient methods of combustion in use at the time meant that only 10 per cent of the heat generated could be used. In 1767, Sweden's Council of the Realm commissioned General Fabian Wrede and the architect Carl Johan Cronstedt to design a more efficient form of domestic heating. Their solution was the Swedish tiled stove.

German-style wood-fired ovens with tiled exteriors had been in use since medieval times. But they did not give off much more heat than an ordinary fireplace. The new Swedish tiled ovens, however, contained an innovative labyrinth of internal flue ducts, up to 10 metres in length. As the smoke and hot air passed through the ducts, it heated up the brickwork and tiles, resulting in nearly 90 per cent heating

Original drawing from Cronstedt & Wrede, 1767.

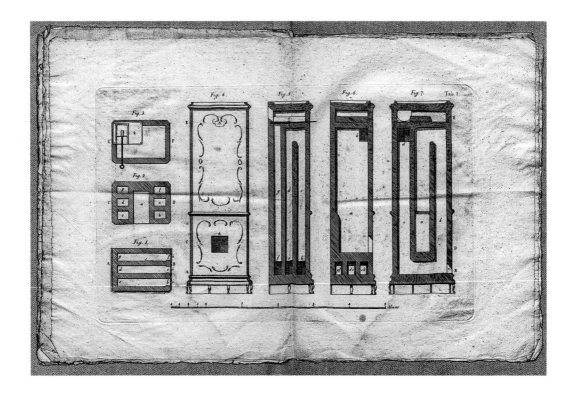

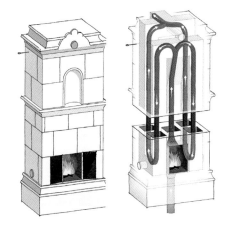

efficiency. Special leaflets were printed with diagrams to spread knowledge of how to construct tiled stoves – an early example of a public-sector awareness campaign for new technology.

Tiled stoves led to changes in home design. Now homes could have larger windows, because heat loss through glass panes was less of a problem. At first, only wealthy people could afford the new form of heating, but tiled stoves became more common in large farmhouses in the 19th century.

The heyday for Swedish tiled stoves came as the nation became more urbanised in the second half of the 19th century. Apartment houses were built for the working and middle classes with tiled stoves as their main source of heating. In the 1920s and 1930s, tiled stoves were replaced by central heating systems. By the 1970s, it was virtually impossible to buy a new tiled stove. Some enterprising builders salvaged old tiled stoves from buildings marked for demolition, but the second-hand market suffered from a lack of experienced manufacturers and repairers.

The Swedish tiled stove did not completely vanish, though. Today's energy crunch has led to a renewed interest. While tiled stoves are hardly the solution to our carbon emissions problem, their efficiency makes them the best choice for people who want to supplement their main home heating system with a real fire. Several Swedish manufacturers now produce modern tiled stoves, and a new generation of craftspeople can install the new models as well as old ones.

The people's advocate

OMBUDSMAN

The Swedish term *ombudsman* has been adopted in many places around the world to denote an official tasked with scrutinising the actions of public authorities on behalf of citizens. The word *ombudsman* comes from the Old Norse *umboðsmaðr*. It has been documented in Danish, Swedish, Norwegian and Icelandic sources since the Middle Ages as a general term for a person who represents another. Sweden's first official ombudsman – the 'Supreme Ombudsman' – was appointed in 1713 by King Charles XII to monitor the running of the country during his exile in Turkey.

That was not the first time in history a ruler appointed some sort of representative to scrutinise his officials, though. In China in the third century bce, the Qin emperor dispatched a 'secret inspector' to check on the provincial management and people's opinions of the authorities. In the Roman Empire, tribunes served similar functions.

But it was Sweden that created the first ombudsman in the modern sense: an official who represents and safeguards citizens' rights and interests vis-à-vis executive authority. That was in 1809, when Sweden adopted a new constitution based on the French philosopher Montesquieu's division of power into three functions: legislative, judicial and executive. The position of Parliamentary Ombudsman, appointed by the Swedish parliament, was created as a counterpart to the Chancellor of Justice, who represented the government.

A new constitution had become necessary as a result of King Gustav IV Adolf's method of ruling. He had, in an unfortunate way, drawn Sweden into the Napoleonic Wars and had lost the territory of Finland – the eastern half of the Swedish Empire – to Russia. In the spring of 1809, a group of leading noblemen rebelled and deposed the king. The Swedish parliament drew up a new constitution, inspired by 18th-century Enlightenment ideals, to prevent a recurrence of the authoritarianism practised by Gustav IV Adolf's father, King Gustav III. One check on the monarch's power was the newly created position of Parliamentary Ombudsman, who would safeguard subjects' rights on behalf of parliament.

Anyone in Sweden can submit a complaint to the ombudsman if they think a public authority has acted unlawfully or arbitrarily or

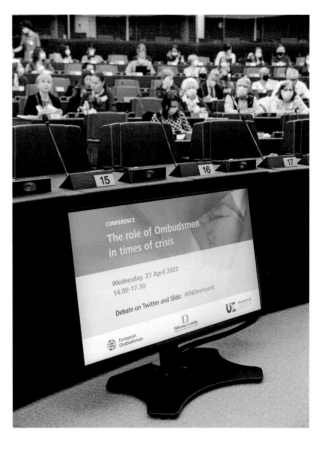

committed an abuse of power. Today, Sweden has five such offices in addition to the original Parliamentary Ombudsman. They deal with areas including disability discrimination and children's rights. Over 80 countries around the world have introduced ombudsmen after this model. In fact, the Swedish word *ombudsman* is used in a number of English-speaking countries, including Australia (*the Commonwealth Ombudsman*), Pakistan (*Federal Ombudsman*) and Ireland (*the Office of the Ombudsman*). The word is also used in Dutch, for *de federale ombudsman*. Other countries have created their own names for the same function, such as France (*le Mediáteur de la République*), Peru (*Defensoría del Pueblo*), Poland (*Rzecznik Praw Obywatelskich*) and Romania (*Avocatul Poporului*), to name just a few.

Ombudsmen play a key role in monitoring the actions of government and public authorities.

Most of these ombudsmen – or ombudspersons, as they are often called nowadays – were established in the last half-century. The first country after Sweden to establish an ombudsman was Finland in 1919. That brought things full circle, since it was the loss of Finland that led to the creation of the office of Sweden's first ombudsman.

Striking a light

SAFETY MATCHES

Hans Christian Andersen's tragic tale 'The Little Match Girl' tells of a poor little girl who doesn't want to go home on New Year's Eve. The weather is freezing cold. She is barefoot and shivering, but she knows her father will beat her for failing to sell any matches. So she huddles in an alley and slowly freezes to death as she lights her matches one by one against a wall for warmth.

But the matches she was selling were not sulphur matches. Sulphur matches, in use for many centuries, cannot be lit by striking them against a rough surface. They require contact with a burning object to ignite. The little girl was actually selling phosphorus friction matches, which may have also contained some sulphur.

Phosphorus matches were invented in the 17th century by the Anglo-Irish chemist and inventor Robert Boyle. They could be ignited via friction but were highly toxic. The match tips were dipped in yellow phosphorus, which is deadly to humans in large doses. Long-term exposure can cause osteonecrosis, a condition in which the bones virtu-

A matchstick-themed float at the Children's Day parade in Stockholm, 1938.

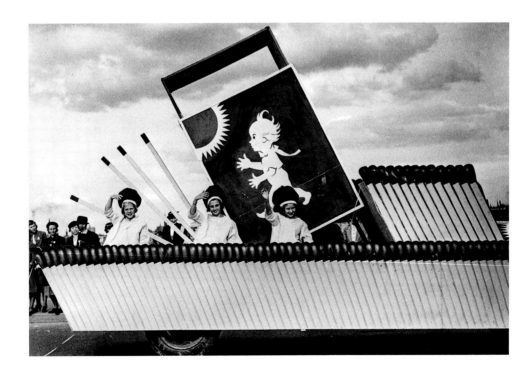

ally dissolve. Phosphorus matches could also spontaneously combust if they rubbed together in their box.

When 'The Little Match Girl' was published in 1845, the old-style sulphur and phosphorus matches were on their way out. A British chemist named John Walker had developed a phosphorus-free match in the early 19th century. It was the first 'safety match' – in this case, 'safety' referred to a lack of danger from poisoning or spontaneous combustion.

Walker's matches were unsafe in a different way, though. When the user drew a match impregnated with potassium chloride and sulphide of antimony through the folded piece of sandpaper included in the packet, the usual result was a momentary spark that quickly fizzled out. For lighting a fire in your fireplace, it was better to use the hazardous phosphorus matches – or the tried-and-true method of flint, steel and tinder.

In the early 1840s, a Swedish chemist by the name of Gustaf Erik Pasch discovered that the toxic yellow phosphorus in match heads could be replaced with red phosphorus, which was practically harmless. This useful replacement had been discovered by Jöns Jacob Berzelius, who was Pasch's lecturer at Uppsala University. Berzelius was an eminent chemist and a member of both the Swedish Academy and the Royal Society in London. He had not managed to find a practical use for his discovery. Pasch realised that replacing the sandpaper in Walker's matchboxes with a red phosphorus surface enabled a match to be lit and used safely.

Pasch, who had suffered terrible tragedy with the loss of his wife, three children, his sister-in-law and mother-in-law in a cholera epidemic in 1834, tried to monetise his invention by becoming a shareholder in a match factory, but the venture was not very successful. Other investors spotted the potential of his discovery, though. It is possible that Johan Lundström, an imaginative entrepreneur who had launched his career by exporting lingonberries and leeches to England, learned of Pasch's research during his time as a student at Uppsala

Less than half of 1 per cent of the energy given off by a match flame is visible light. Most of the rest is in the form of heat.

University. If that is the case, it would make the safety match an early example of cooperation between scientific research and business.

In any case, in 1844, in the town of Jönköping, Johan Lundström and his brother set up a factory to manufacture phosphorus matches. In the early 1850s, the brothers switched production over to Pasch's formula, which they patented. They experimented with different types of wood in their matchsticks and determined that aspen was sustainable and burned evenly. Later, they updated their factory equipment. To maintain the secrecy of their production methods and prevent competitors from copying them, the Lundströms assembled their machinery on site from components purchased from several different suppliers.

The innovation, known in different countries as 'the Swedish safety match', *Schwedenhölzer* and *allumettes suédoises*, had begun to conquer the world. Sweden had as many as 40 factories manufacturing matches. In 1896, the Jönköping match factory's annual production capacity was seven million boxes. Matchboxes came in different designs for different markets. Many boxes sold in the British Empire were labelled with the name 'Three Stars'. Other brand names were 'The Three Cocoa Pods', 'The Three Paddles' and 'The Three Fishes'.

During the First World War, the Jönköping match factory was acquired by Ivar Kreuger, a prominent Swedish businessman. At its peak, Kreuger's global empire included 250 match factories in 43 countries, representing 75 per cent of the world's match production. From this base, Kreuger expanded into financial deals that would lead to his bankruptcy and suicide in Paris in 1932. Safety matches are still around, though they now have competition from butane lighters and various sorts of electronic devices. But in their simple, foolproof form, matches will probably be around for a long time to come.

In 1992 Swedish Match introduced the first sulphur-free matches, which were also free from toxic heavy metals.

Match production near Jönköping in the 1950s.

Making it all go round

THE PROPELLER

After millennia of dependence on wind and manual power, innovative shipbuilders in the late 18th century began to consider how the recently developed steam engine could be harnessed to propel ships. The solution was to transfer the engine's output to a large paddle wheel, which scooped up water and moved the vessel forward.

In the first half of the 19th century, paddle steamers revolutionised transport along rivers and lakes. They were especially popular on the Mississippi River in the United States, where they took passengers and freight up- and downstream between Minneapolis and New Orleans. Some paddle steamers were floating entertainment venues with gambling parlours. They were also used in Europe, including on the Thames. Sweden was also a leader in steamboat travel, thanks to the efforts of an Englishman named Samuel Owen.

Broad-beamed paddle steamboats were not suited to ocean travel. They were also ungainly as warships – partly due to their lack of manoeuvrability, partly because their paddle wheels were easy to shoot off in battle. Was there a way to utilise steam power on the open seas? Enter a Swede by the name of John Ericsson, who would revolutionise seafaring for ever.

Ericsson was born in 1803 in a small mining village called Långbanshyttan in western Sweden. His father Olof was a blasting foreman who helped build the Göta Canal, the 120-mile (190-km) east-west waterway that connects the Baltic Sea with the Kattegat. The project's organiser, Baltzar von Platen, noticed that both John and his elder brother Nils had a talent for engineering. He enrolled them as cadets in the Swedish military engineering corps.

Nils went on to become Sweden's leading canal and railway builder in the 19th century. John rose to become a lieutenant in the

Five-bladed propeller on the USS *Forrestal*, an aircraft carrier in service from 1955 to 1993.

An early propeller on the monitor USS *Dictator* in 1862.

Jämtland ranger regiment in northern Sweden before moving to Britain in 1826. He believed there was more demand in Britain for his inventions.

John Ericsson became a partner in an engineering workshop in England and developed a number of inventions, including a steam fire engine. He also built a locomotive that competed against George Stephenson's famous *Rocket* in trials on the Liverpool–Manchester railway route in October 1829. Ericsson's *Novelty* was in the lead for several days, but suffered a breakdown late in the competition, allowing Stephenson to claim victory.

John Ericsson also considered how steam engines could be employed at sea. Earlier engineering thinkers such as Archimedes and Leonardo da Vinci had designed hydraulic and aerial screws. Inspired by sea birds' webbed feet, Ericsson created the 'goose foot propeller' in 1836. The following year, he created an improved model by replacing the 'goose feet' with blades mounted around a hub. The same basic design is still in use today.

John Ericsson's invention prompted an American businessman to persuade him to go to New York in 1839. Within a few years, 43 vessels were powered by Ericsson's propellers in the United States. The final design had four blades, following experiments with five- and six-bladed versions. The first propeller-driven vessel was built in Sweden in 1843. That same year, a race was organised between the steam-driven frigate USS *Princeton*, equipped with Ericsson's propeller, and the *Great Western*, the fastest paddle wheel steamer to date. The *Princeton* won, and paddle steamers were relegated to history, though a few remained in use on smaller waterways into the 20th century.

Ericsson and his American colleague, who had now started a business together, also hoped to secure commissions from the US Navy. But after an unsuccessful demonstration of a propeller ship during which its cannon exploded, the US government severed contact with the Swedish inventor.

Interest was rekindled during the American Civil War, when Washington DC came under threat from the Confederate ironclad warship *Merrimack*. Ericsson had promised he could deliver a propeller-

driven ironclad ship in 100 days. USS *Monitor* departed the shipyard in Brooklyn on 6 March 1862 bound for Chesapeake Bay, where *Merrimack* was attacking the Union's small flotilla of sailing vessels. After battling to a draw, *Merrimack* broke away and headed into port for repairs. That was enough for *Monitor* to be declared victorious. John Ericsson was hailed as a hero in the Northern states.

John Ericsson lived in New York for the rest of his life, though he always felt Swedish. After his death in 1889, his body was returned to Sweden in accordance with his wishes for burial in Filipstad near the little village where he had been born. A large crowd gathered in New York's Battery Park to say their goodbyes. In Stockholm, tens of thousands lined the streets as the brilliant inventor's coffin was taken from the port to the central railway station for transport to his final resting place.

A century after the age of steam, modern ships are still driven by propellers. Whether they are powered by internal combustion engines or an electric motor, John Ericsson's simple idea continues to convert power into forward motion.

Modern-day ships' propellers have blades pitched to provide more efficient thrust and lower fuel consumption. This propeller, measuring 8.8 m in diameter, was manufactured in Germany in 2004 for one of the world's largest container ships.

A mind sharp as steel

GÖRANSSON AND THE BESSEMER PROCESS

People have been manufacturing steel for nearly 4,000 years. For much of that time, transforming iron into steel was a costly, complex process. The small quantities of steel produced in ancient times were used chiefly for hardened blades on swords, knives and other weapons. Legend has it that when the king of Persia paid tribute to Alexander the Great, his payment was in the form of Damascus steel – reputed to be the finest steel ever made – rather than silver or gold.

In the 17th and 18th centuries, new steel manufacturing processes were developed in Europe, but production capacity was still limited. Demand for steel grew in the 19th century to construct that era's machinery, bridges, railways and buildings. In 1855, the British inventor Henry Bessemer unveiled a new process he said would enable steel production on an industrial scale.

One major challenge was the high carbon content of iron ore: in steel production, carbon levels had to be reduced to between 0.3 and 1 per cent. Bessemer found a way to remove carbon and other undesirable elements by blowing oxygen into molten pig iron.

The technique seemed promising, and soon Bessemer had secured a contract with a British steel mill to produce several thousand tons of steel. There was one problem, though: the technique didn't work in practice. The molten pig iron did not remain hot enough for the oxygenation process to be effective. The resulting steel was porous. Having already licensed his process to a number of companies, Bessemer was forced to buy back all the licences.

This is where Göran Fredrik Göransson enters the picture. He was a wholesaler from Gävle with a range of sidelines. He owned the Högbo ironworks with a blast furnace on Lake Edsken. As a young man in the 1840s, he had spent some years abroad and become proficient in several languages, particularly English. On a business trip to Britain in 1857, he heard about Bessemer's patent and paid £2,000 to acquire a licence to use the process in Sweden.

Göransson installed converter vessels, a blast apparatus and a boiler imported from Britain to start using the new production process at the Edske facility. Just as in previous attempts, though, the results were poor, mainly because the temperature in the vessels was not hot enough.

In the spring of 1858, the Edske blast furnace was rebuilt with fireproof bricks from Höganäs and modifications to the blast flow. These changes helped to achieve a higher, more consistent temperature in the vessel. The Edske plant produced its first successful batch of steel using the Bessemer method in July 1858. It was ready to manufacture steel in the huge quantities needed in the rush to industrialise.

EDSKE MASUGN DEN FÖRSTA LYCKADE BESSEMERBLÅS-
NINGEN UTFÖRD 18 JULI 1858 GENOM G. F. GÖRANSSON

Göransson remained in contact with Bessemer throughout the process, and Bessemer even paid a visit to the Högbo ironworks. But Bessemer showed little appreciation for Göransson, other than a brief mention in a speech to British engineers in May 1859. Without Göransson from Gävle, the Bessemer process would have remained an intriguing theory. Thanks to Göransson's refinements, the process was adopted all over the world. And the little steel mill expanded to become the global corporation Sandvik with nearly 40,000 employees and sales to 160 countries.

On 31 August 2022, Sandvik Materials Technology was hived off from Sandvik AB and listed on the Nasdaq Stockholm stock exchange as Alleima AB. Alleima remains true to its roots with steel as the common denominator in all its products.

Illustration of the first successful batch of steel produced using the Bessemer process in 1858.

Following pages: An updated version of the Bessemer process is still used to smelt stainless steel at the Sandviken steelworks. To minimise the amount of carbon in the molten steel, oxygen is injected with argon or nitrogen gas into the furnace. Steel can be resmelted and recycled any number of times.

An explosive innovation

ALFRED NOBEL AND DYNAMITE

Dynamite was the innovation the 19th century had been waiting for. A new industrialised world was on the horizon but building it would require vast quantities of coal and iron ore. Those resources had to be brought up to the Earth's surface. Roads had to be blasted through mountains, and land had to be levelled for new and ever expanding cities. It called for an explosive innovation.

There were established methods of blasting at that time. For millennia, people had employed fire-setting as a way of breaking rock. That practice involved setting fires to heat the rock, followed by cooling the rock with water to cause it to crack. But that was a slow, labour-intensive method. In the 18th century, people started using gunpowder. It was simpler but still quite inefficient. Clearly, anyone who succeeded in finding a safe, powerful blasting method would become world-famous – and presumably earn a fortune.

In 1847 an Italian chemist by the name of Ascanio Sobrero formulated nitroglycerine by combining nitric acid with glycerol. Nitroglycerine had several advantages over other substances: besides its powerful effectiveness, it generated very little toxic gas in explosions. But Sobrero thought nitroglycerine was too dangerous and unpredictable, so he stopped working with it.

That was not an unreasonable assessment, as the Nobels – a Swedish family of entrepreneurs and inventors – discovered on the morning of Saturday, 3 September 1864, when their laboratory and workshop in Stockholm blew up. Five people died in the explosion, including Emil, the youngest of the four Nobel brothers. His elder brother Alfred, who had been in a different building at the time, escaped with just a few scratches. Their father Immanuel, who had left the laboratory just before the explosion, was also unhurt.

Immanuel, Alfred and Emil had been conducting experiments to find a safe application for nitroglycerine. Immanuel was convinced that

A vintage packet containing 20 sticks of dynamite.

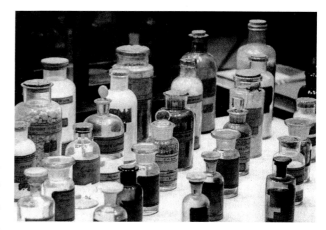

Chemicals in Alfred Nobel's Paris laboratory.

some blend of nitroglycerine with gunpowder would work. Alfred, on the other hand, thought that the gunpowder and nitroglycerine had to be kept separate. Eventually he discovered a method that was promising enough for him to patent it. His method involved inserting a glass tube containing gunpowder into the nitroglycerine. When the gunpowder was ignited by means of a fuse, the glass tube exploded, detonating the nitroglycerine all at once.

That seemed to have solved the problem. Alfred successfully employed his new blasting technique at a mine near Lake Vättern in the summer of 1864. The press wrote about the success and predicted that Nobel's 'blasting oil' would take over from gunpowder in mining operations. Alfred Nobel was quoted as saying that accidents were now 'as good as impossible'. Then came the explosion in Stockholm that September. Nobel ended up in court, and many people regarded nitroglycerine as too dangerous to use.

If Nobel's company was to survive, he would have to find a way to make his 'blasting oil' safer. After various experiments, he tried combining nitroglycerine with a porous material such as sand or coal to make it safe for transport.

Nobel found that he could use diatomaceous earth, a highly absorbent greyish-white sand. However, it was difficult and costly to extract the blasting oil from the sand after transport. Nobel saw another possibility: rather than extracting the nitroglycerine from the sand, he could use the mixture as an explosive. It was hard to ignite, but it would work. The mixture of nitroglycerine and sand was shaped into round sticks the same diameter as drill bits commonly used in mining. The sticks were wrapped in parchment paper so they could be handled easily, with no residue. To detonate the explosive, a copper blasting cap with mercury fulminate and potassium chlorate was placed on the stick and connected to a fuse. Then you just had to light the fuse.

Because even the word 'nitroglycerine' caused many people to shy away, Nobel decided to give his explosive a new name. Inspired by

Werner von Siemens' new electric generator – called a dynamo, after *dynami*, the Greek word for power – Nobel called his innovation 'dynamite'.

Nobel devoted a great deal of time and effort to refining his dynamite. He developed a cooling system for his dynamite factories, because nitroglycerine production generated a lot of heat, thereby increasing the risk of explosion. It was also hazardous to transport nitroglycerine from the production facility to the place where it was mixed with diatomaceous earth. Nobel came up with a simple, brilliant solution. He sited the production facility on a hilltop, so the nitroglycerine could flow down through lead pipes to the building where it was added to the compound.

Alfred Nobel realised early on that there was a global market for dynamite. To avoid the dangers of transporting the material over long distances, he built factories all over the world – first in Scandinavia, then elsewhere in Europe and the United States. Demand for dynamite seemed inexhaustible in a world where people were blasting new tunnels, canals, mines and building foundations at an ever-increasing rate. Soon, Nobel had built a business empire of over a hundred factories.

Alfred Nobel was also skilled at obtaining patents to protect his innovation against competitors and pirate copies. When he died at his home in the Italian town of San Remo on 10 December 1896 at the age of 63, he held more than 350 patents. There was one problem he did not manage to solve, though: the threat of war. Alfred Nobel – a good friend of the prominent peace activist Bertha von Suttner – had hoped that the explosive power of dynamite would be so formidable as to prevent future wars.

Perhaps that's why he used his fortune to establish the Nobel Prize, a group of awards given to people who are deemed to have done the most to benefit humanity during the past year. His establishment of the world's most significant award for discoveries and innovations was perhaps just as great a contribution as the invention of dynamite.

After two millennia of unsuccessful attempts to create a shortcut between the Aegean Sea and the Ionian Sea, engineers used dynamite to construct the Corinth Canal in the late 19th century. Here, the cruise ship MS *Braemar* passes through the canal.

The cream of the crop

DE LAVAL AND THE CENTRIFUGAL SEPARATOR

An advertisement for a separator with the slogan, 'A child can use it'.

In any list of Swedish innovations, there will be a few names that appear more than once. Gustaf de Laval is one of them. A man of unwavering self-confidence and great impatience, he embarked on one project after another. He has 92 patents, 37 companies and a total of around 200 inventions to his credit. Of those inventions, the centrifugal separator and the steam turbine are among the most significant.

Gustaf de Laval was born in the spring of 1845 in the town of Orsa in Sweden's central Dalarna province. He was born into a highly regarded, successful family of noble lineage. His father came from a long line of military figures, while his mother's side boasted industrialists, scientists, doctors and artists. Gustaf attended school in the town of Falun and then continued his studies at what is now KTH Royal Institute of Technology in Stockholm. He received a degree in mechanical engineering in 1866. Despite de Laval's excellent grades, jobs were hard to come by for engineers at that time. The country was in the grips of a depression, and much of the population suffered from poverty and hunger. After a few short-term jobs, de Laval decided to return to study. With grants from the House of Nobility and support from his family, he enrolled at Uppsala University and received his doctorate in 1872 – also with distinction.

Gustaf de Laval secured employment in a mining district near Falun. He had previously worked there on short-term projects, but now he was a fully fledged engineer. He was involved in plans for a sulphuric acid production facility and sketched out a method to employ a centrifuge in moulding glass bottles. A new factory was launched to manufacture bottles using his method, but the company foundered and closed down after just a few months. At this point, Gustaf de Laval was in debt to the tune of 40,000 *riksdaler*. Miraculously, he managed to pay off the entire sum in 10 years – all thanks to his outstanding creativity, combined with a refusal to be cowed by setbacks.

His inventions came in quick succession. When a couple of his patented innovations – including a 'New Grate for Bessemer Furnace' and a 'Device for Galvanising Iron Plates' – had a decisive impact on Klosters Ironworks' fortunes, the head of the company invited him

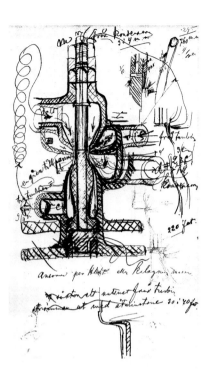

Sketch from Gustaf de Laval's notebook showing how his separator would separate cream from milk.

over for dinner one evening. The plant owner also had a farm, and he had recently read in a German dairy journal about a new method of separating cream from milk. When he heard about the method, de Laval is said to have exclaimed: 'I'll show you that centrifugal force works the same way in Sweden as in Germany!' He embarked on various ways to utilise centrifuges.

In those days, the usual practice was to let fresh milk stand until the cream, which was lighter than milk, rose to the top of the container and could be skimmed off. Gustaf de Laval wanted to speed up the process, so he poured some milk into a vessel which was then spun round. The spinning caused the cream to separate from the milk because the heavier milk was pressed against the walls of the vessel while the cream remained in the centre. The vessel was fitted with two outlet pipes, one for the cream and one for the milk. Simple, really.

Perhaps the bad experiences from the bottle factory were still fresh in the owner's mind, because he did not share de Laval's enthusiasm and refused to invest in this invention. So Laval set off for Stockholm with the words: 'You'll be hearing from me!' With help from a cousin, he obtained funding and access to a factory. Further refinements were made to the device, and a few years later Laval had constructed a continuously operating machine which he called a 'centrifugal separator', or just a 'separator'. It was not the only milk separator of its kind in the world, but de Laval's device had the advantage of being cheap and easy to use. Ordinary farmers soon took an interest. Advertisements showed a picture of a farm girl turning its handle.

In 1883, Gustaf de Laval founded the AB Separator company, which is now part of the Alfa Laval corporation. By 1905, over half a million separators had been sold to farmers all over the world. They played a major role in industrialisation.

His work on the separator helped de Laval understand the need for a machine that could maintain a high, consistent rotation speed. He started experimenting with steam and turbines. Soon he had devised a steam turbine that could achieve 30,000–40,000 rpm. When it became apparent that such high speeds damaged the axles, he constructed and patented a new type of shock absorber. He also developed a nozzle that could utilise the kinetic energy of steam. Today, that nozzle is called a de Laval nozzle and is used in rocket engines.

With remarkable energy and drive, Gustaf de Laval continued to come up with even more innovations in the wake of challenges his inventions gave rise to.

A device to measure the fat content of milk, an 'emulsor' to return fat to skimmed milk, various milking machines and a butter churn – these are just some of the innovations de Laval developed following the success of the separator. But he also had large-scale ideas such as aircraft, hovercraft, space rockets, self-driving vehicles and various other ways to utilise electrical power. He also took an interest in social issues and served as a member of parliament for a couple of terms.

Gustaf de Laval's creativity came at the cost of his businesses' management and finances. After his death in 1913, his widow Isabel had the difficult task of filing for bankruptcy on behalf of his estate. While he was not financially successful, de Laval possessed a remarkable drive throughout his life. As the epitaph on his gravestone says, he was 'the man of high speeds'.

The cream separator designed by Gustaf de Laval was simple to use. It was a huge success: by the early 20th century, over half a million separators had been sold to farmers all over the world.

Advertisement from *Farmer's Magazine*, 1920.

CENTRUM

A gripping story

ADJUSTABLE SPANNER

One day in the late 1880s, Johan Petter Johansson could not find a single pipe wrench in his engineering workshop in Enköping. His employees were all working on remote jobs and had taken the workshop's entire set of fixed pipe wrenches along with them. That quandary would eventually lead to one of the world's most practical inventions: the adjustable spanner (wrench).

Johansson solved the problem of his missing pipe wrenches by fabricating a wrench with jaws that could be adjusted to fit the dimensions of a pipe. In 1888 he obtained a patent on his invention, called the plumber's wrench. It quickly became a commercial success. He then turned his attention to fixed spanners for nuts and bolts.

For centuries, blacksmiths had forged long-handled tools for gripping and turning various types of threaded metal parts. One early use was for assembling knights' suits of armour, but perhaps their most important purpose was to tighten wagon wheels to prevent them from coming loose. Initially, nuts and spanners were made individually, but production started to become fairly standardised in the 19th century. People could purchase sets of spanners in common sizes.

Inventors also started experimenting with various types of adjustable spanners. In 1842, an English engineer named Richard Clyburn created a version with two moveable jaws that could be adjusted by means of a screw. It is unclear whether Johansson knew about Clyburn's invention. In any case, Johansson obtained a Swedish patent on a similar tool in 1891.

While an adjustable spanner with two moveable jaws is more convenient than a fixed spanner, it is also weaker. The jaws could break if too much torque was applied. So Johansson improved on

One of the very first adjustable spanners made by J.P. Johansson, patented in 1892.

his original design by making one of the jaws fixed and one moveable by means of a screw device. In 1892 he obtained a patent on this adjustable spanner, which is essentially the same model still in use all over the world. In Denmark, it is commonly called a *svensknøgle* (meaning 'Swedish key'), while the Russian and Hebrew nicknames for the tool translate as 'little Swede'.

Today Bahco, the company founded by Johan Petter Johansson, has sold more than 100 million adjustable spanners. Johansson handed the business over to his sons in 1916 so he could devote more time to his inventions. He obtained more than 110 patents, but the adjustable spanner was his most significant innovation.

Johansson also has fans who celebrate him for his sugar tongs. They came about after his wife complained when he came in straight from the workshop and used his dirty fingers to pick up a sugar lump from the bowl for his coffee. Even if the sugar tongs did not have the same impact as the adjustable plumber's wrench and the adjustable spanner, it is yet another example of a Swedish inventor's ability to draw inspiration from the practical problems of everyday life rather than dream of revolutionary creations.

Aviation pioneer Katherine Sai-Fun Choung uses an adjustable spanner to tighten a nut in Los Angeles in 1933.

Power on a large scale

THREE-PHASE ELECTRIC POWER

Electricity is indispensable to modern lifestyles. Most aspects of society depend on it. But electricity has to be transmitted to where it's needed. That's where Jonas Wenström's invention comes in.

Jonas Wenström was a remarkable person. As a young child in the 1850s, he suffered from rickets. The disease weakened and deformed his bones, causing his body to take on a hunched appearance. But despite his fragile body, he possessed a powerful mind.

As the son of an engineer in the small industrial town of Hällefors in Örebro county, he was around all sorts of mechanical constructions from an early age. He was a bright pupil and continued his studies at the universities of Uppsala and Oslo in the 1870s. Study trips to Germany, France and the United States expanded his horizons even further, making it clear to him that electricity was the future. Gas

Hällsjön hydroelectric plant, 1884. Alternating current and transformers allowed the electricity generated here to be transmitted across greater distances. Industries no longer needed to be located adjacent to power generation facilities. Sweden still gets around 40 per cent of its electri-city from hydroelectric power.

lighting and paraffin lamps were still the norm, but many European engineers were turning their attention to lighting sparked by electricity. Wenström began experimenting with a rudimentary light bulb, but word reached him that Thomas Edison had applied for a patent on his own version. Wenström wrote, 'It was with mixed emotions that I received news of Edison's latest invention. It was certainly reassuring that my idea was feasible, but of course it was disheartening that I was not in a position to bring my invention to fruition.'

Instead, Wenström started to think about what would happen if industries also wanted to use electricity as a power source. More electricity would have to be generated – and then transmitted across long distances. By 1882 he had obtained a patent on a generator or dynamo machine, which he nicknamed 'the turtle'.

This device and Wenström's other patents were crucial in the growth of ASEA, an engineering company founded in Västerås in 1890. Wenström played an active role in the company, producing a number of dynamos and other machines. The direct current produced by a dynamo was hard to transmit over long distances. Wenström thought long and hard about that problem.

He ended up working with alternating current, but that choice was not a foregone conclusion. In the 1890s, direct current and alternating current each had their advocates. Thomas Edison and General Electric were in favour of direct current, while Nikola Tesla and Westinghouse argued for alternating current.

Advocates of direct current claimed that alternating current could be dangerous. Edison even tried to discredit those arguing in favour of alternating current by staging public 'executions' of animals in a sort of electric chair powered by alternating current.

The best argument in favour of alternating current was that it could be transmitted over long distances by means of power transformers. In the end, that was the deciding factor. Edison had to admit defeat as alternating current won the 'electric war'.

Alternating current can be transformed into high voltages, which

Jonas Wenström never stopped improving his designs. In power plants like this one in the late 19th century, a steam-driven fly-wheel drove a dynamo (generator) by means of a belt.

can then be distributed over long transmission lines without too much loss of power. This system requires transformers, which were invented by William Stanley in 1879.

Jonas Wenström's innovation was to feed the alternating current through *three* conductors with a 120-degree phase shift. That produced a rotating magnetic field that could run an electric motor.

Wenström's notebooks show that he had completed the calculations for his first three-phase generator in October 1889. A year later, he applied for a patent and quickly constructed a generator, transformer and motor. Time was of the essence, because the Russian engineer Mikhail Dolivo-Dobrovolsky was working on a similar project in a German lab. Wenström and ASEA were granted a patent on the three-phase system, but there were some subsequent legal disputes.

Sweden's first three-phase alternating current system was constructed in 1893. The plan was to set up a large-scale power transmission line to transfer 300 horsepower (220 kilowatts) from a hydroelectric plant to a mine some 15 kilometres away. In the course of his intense work, Jonas Wenström became ill with a lung infection. Just three days after the system started operating, he died at the age of 38.

Wenström never got the chance to marvel at the dizzying technological advances that followed. The introduction of three-phase current was accompanied by the construction of large hydroelectric plants, which enabled Sweden's rapid electrification. That in turn provided a head start for many Swedish manufacturers and businesses.

Today, Sweden is served by an extensive power grid. The large power transmission lines that criss-cross the country carry electricity at 400 kilovolts, which is then stepped down to 230 volts for household use.

Even so, transmission capacity is insufficient for the demands now placed on the power grid. Transport is increasingly moving away from fossil fuels to electricity, and industry requires a reliable supply of electricity 24/7. Demand for electricity could double in the next two decades. Phasing out nuclear power in southern Sweden and the consequences of the new security situation mean that renewable

energy sources like hydroelectricity, wind, solar and biomass are not sufficient to meet demand. What's more, the power grid's limited capacity to transmit electricity from northern Sweden to the south results in large discrepancies in electricity prices.

Meanwhile, major investments are being made in the smart grid, where Sweden plays a world-leading role in research and development. The smart grid incorporates more renewable energy while enabling electricity to be transmitted in both directions. This allows a greater degree of load adjustment and therefore more efficient use. Electricity consumers take on a more active role, both as producers (with solar panels and wind power) and consumers (by means of smart meters). Hopefully, the result will be not only a more secure power network, but also a system that makes us independent of fossil fuels and the geopolitical insecurity they entail.

Three-phase power enables electricity to be transmitted across long distances.

To the lighthouse

THE SUN VALVE

'It won't work.' That was Thomas Edison's spontaneous assessment of one of Gustaf Dalén's most important innovations. Edison was wrong, as it turned out. The sun valve did work. Besides turning a lighthouse beam on and off automatically, it was very reliable and required no maintenance. Blockhusudden Lighthouse, one of several near Stockholm, was the first to install a sun valve in 1912. When the lighthouse was converted to electricity in 1980, workers were amazed to discover that the sun valve had never been repaired.

Gustaf Dalén amassed 99 patents to his name, but he is primarily remembered for the Dalén light, which features a sun valve. The Dalén light was ready for use in 1907. Before that, Dalén had come up with a number of innovations to improve lighthouses, thereby improving safety at sea.

In his younger days, Dalén had received some words of wisdom from none other than Gustaf de Laval, another of Sweden's leading innovators, who advised Dalén to obtain a solid education in engineering. After successful studies at Chalmers University of Technology in Gothenburg and the Federal Polytechnical School in Zurich, Dalén secured employment with Svenska Karbid och Acetylen AB, a manufacturer of acetylene gas and other industrial chemicals. The company produced acetylene by means of a chemical reaction between calcium carbide and water. Gustaf Dalén wondered whether the highly combustible gas could be used in lighthouses. That question became his first big challenge, and he threw himself into finding an answer.

Acetylene burns with a bright, hot flame. Even so, vast quantities would be needed for use in lighthouses. How could it be used safely? It was highly explosive. Dalén constructed a system that portioned out the gas in small 'clips' rather than all at once. The small doses were ignited one after another in a continuous series.

The result was a flashing light that required nearly 90 per cent less gas than previous models. Better still, the rate of flashing could be varied to give each lighthouse a distinctive flashing speed, thus aiding navigation even further.

Lighthouse inspector Percy Wood checks a sun valve at Northfleet Upper Lighthouse in the Thames estuary in south-east England.

By then, Gustaf Dalén had risen to become managing director and renamed the company AGA, short for 'Svenska AB Gasaccumulator'. His gas-dosing apparatus was a success and made it feasible to use expensive acetylene gas in lighthouses. But Dalén was not satisfied. It was wasteful to have lighthouses flashing – and consuming gas – in daylight.

Dalén considered the simple fact that a dark-coloured surface will absorb more heat from the sun than a light-coloured one. And heat makes materials expand. So he constructed a valve with a black rod surrounded by three polished rods. The black rod is connected to the valve that can open and close the gas supply. When the sun is shining, the black rod heats up and expands, cutting off the flow of gas. The rod only has to expand by a fraction of a millimetre to shut off the lighthouse's beam. As night falls, the rod shrinks, allowing the gas to flow again. The lighthouse is illuminated.

The sun valve revolutionised lighthouses all over the world. Suddenly, unmanned lighthouses were feasible, when they had been unthinkable just a few years before. New lighthouses were constructed in hazardous locations. A major breakthrough came in 1911, when Dalén secured a large order to supply sun valves for the Panama Canal construction project. With Dalén's sun valve, lighthouses only had to be resupplied with gas cylinders a few times a year. The rest of the time they went on and off automatically. But sun valves were even installed in manned lighthouses, where they made lighthouse-keepers' jobs easier. Over the years, Dalén's sun valve is thought to have prevented thousands of shipwrecks.

Gustaf Dalén showed an early talent for coming up with ways to control and direct processes. Like many 13-year-olds, he had a hard time getting up in the morning. So he made some modifications to an old clock his father had given him. He added a bit of metal and a cylinder covered in sandpaper to the clockwork so that it would strike a match 15 minutes before his alarm was set to go off. The match was suspended above a gas lamp that warmed a pot of coffee. When his clock went off, the light was already on and his room was filled with the aroma of coffee.

Life can sometimes be unkind, too. Dalén suffered a horrible accident on 27 September 1912. He was experimenting to see how much acetylene could be compressed in a heated glass flask when one of the flasks exploded. Dalén survived, but the accident blinded him. The Royal Swedish Academy of Sciences had been planning to award that year's Nobel Prize in Physics to someone with a longer record in research, but they pivoted and awarded it to Dalén instead. He valued his employees at AGA and gave a large chunk of his prize money to them in the form of salary bonuses. Even though he had lost his sight, he remained in charge of the company for another 25 years. The AGA company is also famous in many parts of the world for its low-maintenance, fuel-efficient AGA cooking range.

The Skerryvore Lighthouse in the Hebrides off Scotland's west coast was equipped with a sun valve early on to ensure it would come on as darkness fell.

Smooth operating

BALL BEARINGS

If the city of Gothenburg hadn't been built on a thick layer of clay soil, the Swedish engineer Sven Wingquist wouldn't have invented the self-aligning ball bearing. Then again, maybe he would have – it's difficult to tell how much inspiration an inventor draws from within, and how much comes from their external circumstances.

In the early 20th century, Wingquist was a young maintenance engineer at the Gamlestadens Fabriker textile mill. He faced a problem: the mill's large looms, which were operated by steam engines via long drive shafts that went right up into the roof. The drive shaft bearings kept breaking down, and replacements had to be ordered from abroad. Wingquist determined that the breakdowns were caused by barely perceptible settling of the ground, which slightly shifted the drive shaft beyond the tolerance of the bearings. The result was that the machinery would jam, increasing the risk of fire.

The principle of roller bearings had been known since ancient times, when the Egyptians transported massive stones over cylindrical logs to build the pyramids. The Romans refined the technology by using wooden spheres for tasks like rotating statue plinths – which apparently was a fairly common activity in the Roman Empire. Leonardo da Vinci – yes, him again – was the first person to set out the theoretical principle of ball bearings in his famous notebooks. But ball bearings did not come into widespread use until the 19th century, first in horse-drawn carriages and bicycles, followed by industrial machinery with moving parts.

Wingquist had trained as a textile engineer and spent some time working in the United States. He kept abreast of new international developments. Around the turn of the 20th century, a debate raged about what sort of friction bearing was superior: slide bearings, in which all the parts of a moving machine slid against each other with a layer of oil or grease to lubricate them; or ball bearings, in which metal spheres rolled around in a track, called a raceway.

In 1902 Richard Stribeck, a German professor of metallurgy, presented evidence that a ball bearing was more efficient. That led Wingquist to consider possible improvements that could protect ball bearings from wear and tear when they were subjected to pressure

Ball bearings help reduce friction and improve reliability – thereby saving energy. SKF has manufactured ball bearings of all sizes since 1907.

Following pages: Bearings more than 2 metres across are installed in a cable drum for NOV, a Norwegian offshore energy company.

on their raceway, such as when the ground settled. Wingquist set up an experimental workshop near the textile mill. In 1906 he took out a patent on a spherical ball bearing. The raceway in which the ball assembly moved was rounded, which made it less sensitive to lateral pressure. However, this ball bearing performed less well under axial loads – that is, movement in the same direction as the rolling of the ball assembly.

The mill's executives, who had been sceptical of Wingquist's ambitions at first, realised that their young engineer was on to something. They contributed start-up capital for a subsidiary to develop his ideas. The new company was called Svenska Kullagerfabriken ('Swedish Ball-Bearing Factory'), or SKF for short.

In the spring of 1907, Wingquist submitted a patent application for a multi-row, self-adjusting radial ball bearing. Its distinguishing feature was its two rows of balls, with a raceway in the outer ring that enabled the bearing to withstand axial pressure. The invention was widely known as a 'self-aligning ball bearing' and it made SKF into one of Sweden's most successful companies. Wingquist, always thinking ahead, had also patented his invention in other major industrial countries. With subsidiaries in Germany, the UK and the United States, SKF became a global leader.

Today, we are surrounded by ball bearings. They are inside our washing machines, vacuum cleaners, fans, computers and many other devices in our homes. An average household will contain between 100 and 200 ball bearings. Some of them are tiny. The smallest ball bearing is around half a millimetre across. But there are also huge slewing bearings, such as the one with a diameter of 13 metres that is part of a Canadian oil-drilling rig. Ball bearings are also used to protect buildings against earthquakes. For example, the San Francisco airport stands on a large number of piles, each of which rests on a ball bearing measuring 1.5 metres in diameter.

Assembling roller bearings in 1959. Roller bearings are a variation on ball bearings. Both types of bearings need to support heavy loads, so they are manufactured from vacuum-treated steel free from cracks and impurities.

The measure of man

GAUGE BLOCKS AND THE STANDARD INCH

Precise measurements and international standards are things we take for granted today – and they are indispensable in safe, modern manufacturing. But before a Swede by the name of Carl Edvard Johansson came along, precise measurements were a utopian fantasy. One example of this is the inch.

A unit called an 'inch' had been in use since Roman times to measure length, width and height. It was part of a Swedish system in which 12 inches made a foot, 24 inches made an *aln* (similar to an ell), 72 inches made one fathom and 120 inches made one rod. All of that is clear enough, apart from one thing: how long is one inch?

As long as measurements didn't need to be terribly precise or standardised, it worked well enough to say that an inch was equivalent to the width of a man's thumb. But after the onset of the industrial age, that was too arbitrary. That prompted many countries to adopt the metric system, which had been devised during the French Revolution.

The metric system did not take over everywhere, though. In Greece it was not officially adopted until 1959. A bigger problem was that two of the world's leading industrial nations – the UK and the United States – continued to stick with the old system. But even they were forced to define a standard inch in relation to the metric system. Unfortunately, the British and Americans could not agree on a joint standard, so the American inch was defined as 25.4000508 millimetres, while the British inch was fixed at 25.399977 – and they had different reference temperatures.

It would take an impartial outsider to settle things between them. Enter Carl Edvard Johansson, born in the province of Västmanland in 1864. He was familiar with the American inch after spending some time working in US engineering workshops. He returned to Sweden and got a job with a gun manufacturer in 1888. The factory tried to build every gun of a particular model to the same dimensions. But their measuring implements were not consistent or precise enough. Johansson came up with the idea of creating sets of gauge blocks that could be combined to achieve precise measurements.

The factory lacked precision grinders capable of producing the gauge blocks Johansson had in mind, so he modified his wife's sewing

One of Carl Edvard Johansson's own gauge sets – one of the earliest examples of a succesful standardisation. Users could combine various gauge blocks to achieve precise dimensions.

machine into a grinder. He produced sets of gauge blocks at home in the evenings after his regular shifts at the gun factory.

Finally, he created a set of gauge blocks that could be combined in 20,000 different ways, accurate to 0.01 millimetre. Manufacturers could use a single set of gauge blocks instead of a whole range of measuring devices.

After some complications, Johansson was granted a patent on his gauge block set. In 1907 he started producing the sets for sale. They were an almost instant success as an international standard in all kinds of precision manufacturing.

He also managed to solve the problem of the different standard inches in Britain and America along the way. Johansson's inch – which was 25.4 millimetres at a temperature of 20 degrees Celsius – was adopted as the standard in both countries.

American industry welcomed the standardised inch measurement. 'There are only two people I take off my hat to. One is the President of the United States and the other is Mr Johansson from Sweden,' said Henry M. Leland, the founder of the Cadillac automotive company, in the early 1920s. When Leland's gauge block set was not in use to calibrate equipment on the factory floor, he kept it in his safe.

In 1918, Johansson founded a company in the United States to produce his gauge block sets. They are still in use today and are often called 'Jo-blocks'. When Johansson's company ran into financial difficulties, he was hired by Henry Ford in 1923. Ford relocated Johansson's workshop from New York to Michigan to manufacture his gauge block sets.

Meanwhile, the Royal Swedish Academy of Engineering Sciences had identified a need for standards to ensure consistency and efficiency in manufacturing and trade. Together with Sweden's National Federation of Industry, the Academy set up the Swedish Industrial Commission for Standardisation in 1922.

Parts for assembly line production had to be manufactured to identical dimensions. Henry Ford used Johansson's gauge blocks in his car factories and was so delighted that he provided Johansson with his own workshop at Ford.

Mind the gap

ZIP FASTENER

For centuries, people had to put up with fiddly belts, buttons and hook-and-eye fasteners. The invention of a quick, secure, gap-free means of fastening clothing and other fabric items brought about an often-ignored sartorial revolution. Nowadays, this clever innovation is something we use every day. A hundred years ago, though, zips were high-tech.

More than 1.2 million Swedes – nearly a fifth of Sweden's total population – emigrated to North America between the mid-19th century and the 1920s. One of those who emigrated was a young engineer by the name of Gideon Sundbäck. He left Sweden in 1906 in search of a better future in the United States. Soon he secured a job in a factory owned by Whitcomb Judson, an inventor, in Meadville, Pennsylvania. Sundbäck met Peter A. Aronsson, another engineer with Swedish roots who was already employed there. The factory manufactured an early version of zip fasteners with rows of hooks and eyes sewn individually on to strips of fabric. They were both fiddly and impractical. What's more, these fasteners could pop apart, resulting in embarrassing situations if someone's dress suddenly gaped open or their skirt fell down.

The two Swedish engineers set their minds to improving the device. In 1913, Gideon Sundbäck took out a patent on his first zip fastener. It worked smoothly, with two rows of metal teeth, each sewn on a fabric strip, that opened and closed simply by pulling a slider along the rows. Sundbäck continued to refine the construction, and his next patent – for the 'Hookless #2' model – became the zip that we still use today. He also invented a machine that could manufacture zips automatically.

Both Sundbäck and Aronsson were convinced of the excellence of their creation, but success was not immediate. Four years later, the US Navy took an interest in the new technology and ordered tens of thousands of zips for use in duffle bags and sleeping bags. Orders soon followed from the US Air Force, where pilots had discovered that zips on their uniforms enabled them to adjust their clothing easily in the confines of a cockpit. In the years after the First World War, zips started to be used in all sorts of garments, from delicate petticoats to heavy

Gideon Sundbäck's own technical drawings of his zip fastener that would go on to be a familiar object all over the world.

1,219,881.

Patented Mar. 20, 1917.

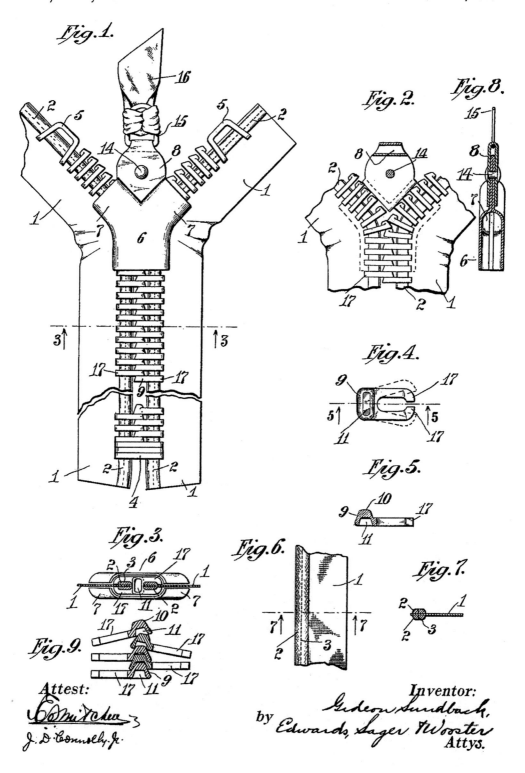

Fig.1.

Fig.2.

Fig.8.

Fig.4.

Fig.5.

Fig.3.

Fig.6.

Fig.7.

Fig.9.

Attest:

Inventor:
Gideon Sundback.
by Edwards, Sager & Wooster
Attys.

winter jackets. The slogan Sundbäck came up with early on captured their convenience: *'Opening like a smile, closing like a line drawn on water.'*

Zips even made their way to Hollywood. Soon, filmmakers started to use them as an erotic symbol. Images of trains disappearing into tunnels were replaced with zips being undone in a slow, sensual movement. Hook-and-eye closures never had that power of attraction.

That brings us to another connection between the two Swedish engineers in Pennsylvania – when Gideon Sundbäck married Peter A. Aronsson's daughter Elvira.

Zips are available in many sizes and for countless uses. Today, there are even water-tight models.

Keeping cool
THE REFRIGERATOR

Keeping food fresh has been a challenge for people throughout history. As soon as our ancestors killed an animal, the battle against spoilage began. People came up with various methods of preserving food, such as salting, smoking, drying and pickling. But it was the modern refrigerator that transformed our access to fresh food all year round.

For a long time, people stored food in hollows filled with ice to keep it cool. Rural farmers had earth-sheltered root cellars outdoors or beneath a hatch in the kitchen floor. In Swedish cities in the 19th century, it was common to have an icebox, cooled by a block of ice, in one's kitchen. That practice continued until well into the 20th century as the forerunner of today's refrigerators.

Baltzar von Platen was born in 1898 in Ystad on Sweden's southern coast. His parents were intellectuals, and prominent guests often came to visit. The outspoken, questioning style of conversation he grew up with stood in contrast to the educational ideals of the day. Baltzar's forthrightness and creativity might have been harnessed better today, but as a pupil he often received poor marks from his teachers. Despite that resistance, he finished his schooling and moved to Stockholm to begin his studies at what is now KTH Royal Institute of Technology.

There, Baltzar von Platen found that his personality served him well. Before long, he found a like-minded friend in Carl Munters, the son of an engineer. They shared an apartment, which they transformed into a laboratory for various projects and inventions. They sometimes overslept and missed important lectures, but they nevertheless managed to complete their studies.

Both young men were interested in refrigeration. They decided to tackle the challenge of how to move heat from a colder place to a warmer place. They needed a coolant and a pump. The coolant changes from a liquid to a vapour as it warms up from the air inside the refrigerator, which then becomes colder. The tubes on the back of the refrigerator become warmer as the coolant is pumped around.

The first prototype was rather large and bulky, but it could maintain a temperature of -40 degrees Celsius. Munters and von Platen continued to refine their invention, and they submitted their refrigeration

It's hard to imagine living without a fridge or freezer now, but only became affordable and commonplace in the 1950s.

device as a joint thesis project in 1922. They also applied for a patent on it. Compared to previous refrigeration equipment, their device was quieter and more adaptable – it could run on electricity, gas or kerosene. They used ammonia as the coolant.

Axel Wenner-Gren, the founder of Electrolux, soon noticed the potential of the students' project. He acquired the rights and hired the young innovators. By 1925 the company was mass-producing the 'absorption refrigerator'.

The advent of the refrigerator came at a time when increasing numbers of households had access to electricity. Swedish homes could be modernised – starting in the kitchen. Refrigeration also enabled global cold chains for food transport. Retailers' chilled cabinets filled with food from around the world, and restaurants offered exotic new dishes. Meals and interest in cooking developed hand in hand with refrigeration technology.

The use of ammonia was a problem, though. To avoid toxic leaks of ammonia gas when a refrigerator broke down, manufacturers switched to freon, a chlorofluorocarbon (CFC) compound. But, as so often in the history of technology, solving one problem created another.

FRIGELUX
le froid domestique à votre service

In the 1980s scientists discovered that CFCs destroy the vital ozone layer in the Earth's atmosphere that protects us from the sun's harmful ultraviolet rays. An international consortium drew up a system of regulations to deal with the problem. The regulations, known as the Montreal Protocol, are often cited as an example of meaningful global environmental agreements that can be achieved. In 1993, Electrolux was the first company to launch a CFC-free refrigerator. CFCs were banned from most uses in 2000 and have been phased out.

At first, Swedish fridges were sold under different brand names in many countries, such as Frigelux in France. Since 1957, the Electrolux brand has been used in all markets.

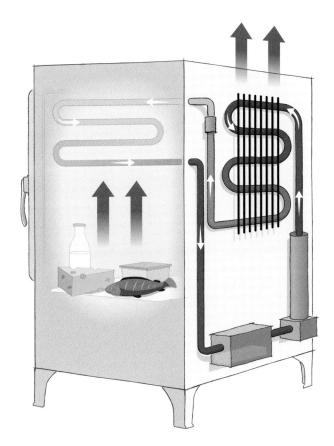

Energy efficiency has also increased significantly. Today's refrigerators use a compressor to circulate the coolant in a closed system, which drastically reduces electricity consumption. A refrigerator today uses just a quarter of the electricity compared to 15 years ago.

After his success with the refrigerator, Baltzar von Platen continued working tirelessly on new inventions. In the mid-1970s he confidently presented every inventor's dream: an eternal source of inexhaustible energy. He was not granted a patent on his perpetual motion machine, but he remained undaunted, telling his critics: 'There are two groups who dismiss my invention. Those who have not read my dissertation. And those who have misread it.'

How did things turn out for Carl Munters? After the success of the refrigerator, he continued creating new inventions by utilising the laws of thermodynamics in creative ways. He obtained nearly 1,000 patents, mainly in the fields of air conditioning and dehumidifying. In 1955, he founded Munters, a company that remains a global leader in climate control. Just as the spirit of Baltzar von Platen lives on at Electrolux, Carl Munters' legacy continues to inspire young engineers to dare to think differently and challenge old assumptions.

Lightweight yet strong
AERATED CONCRETE

Anyone who has stood under the vast dome of the Pantheon in Rome has gazed in awe at its magnificent structure. How could he Romans, working more than 2,000 years ago, build a dome 43 metres across and weighing over 4,000 tons that's strong enough to remain standing to this day? The answer lies in a material whose name is as solid as the stuff itself: concrete.

Nowadays we have many different types of concrete to choose from: fibre-reinforced concrete, steel-reinforced concrete, concrete floor screed, fast-setting concrete, underwater concrete, pervious concrete, shotcrete and various forms of aerated concrete ... All of them are essentially made from the same ingredients the Romans used: sand, aggregate and water, with cement as a binder. The Romans used burnt lime and volcanic ash – they preferred the very fine pozzolanic ash found near Mount Vesuvius. Today we know that pozzolanic ash, also called pozzolana, is a silicate material containing silicon and oxygen atoms.

Silicon is one of the most common elements in the Earth's crust. It is present in alum shale, a geological formation created from sediments of dead plants, algae and other organisms that lived 500 million years ago. It is no accident that one of the major innovations in the history of concrete came about in Sweden, where alum shale formations are common.

Axel Eriksson, born in 1880, studied architecture at what is now KTH Royal Institute of Technology in Stockholm. After advanced studies in the Department of Building Engineering, he got a job as assistant to Professor Henrik Kreüger. As an eager young construction engineer, Eriksson couldn't have found a better place to work. Kreüger enjoyed a high profile at that time. He was the consulting engineer on the Stockholm Olympic Stadium, built for the 1912 summer games, and a number of other landmark buildings such as Stockholm City Hall and the Stockholm Public Library. Together with his cousin, the engineer, financier and industrialist Ivar Kreuger, he introduced reinforced concrete – now the most common building material in the world – to Sweden. Ivar Kreuger would later become known as the 'matchstick king' whose financial house of cards ultimately came crashing down in 1932 (see page 30).

Fuel was in short supply during the First World War, and there was a need for a construction material that could take the place of wood. It should also require less energy to produce than brick and better insulating properties than concrete. A tough set of requirements.

Axel Eriksson took up the challenge. He started by examining the properties of concrete in minute detail, testing various mixtures of shale, cement and aluminium powder. He conducted a series of experiments in a chamber where he could control the pressure, temperature and humidity.

Something very surprising happened when he applied both high pressure and high temperature to the concrete. Its structure

Post-war construction in Sweden was made easier with aerated concrete. It was cheap and easy to handle.

suddenly changed. The concrete filled up with air bubbles, making it highly porous. Eriksson also found that a more stable product resulted if he subjected the blue-grey material to a steam pressure hardening process before drying it. After curing, the concrete block resembled a blue-grey bath sponge. Was it actually concrete or something altogether different he had created?

Axel Eriksson announced his creation in a scientific article in 1922. Two years later he submitted a patent application for aerated concrete, which has been known by several names, including autoclaved concrete, cellular concrete and porous concrete, and by the brand name Ytong in Sweden. Commercial production started in 1929 in a brand-new factory commissioned by the industrialist Carl August Carlén. It was a bold investment in a project that carried high risks for both men. Could production be scaled up? And would customers

Aerated concrete blocks can be cut with an ordinary saw. They provide greater fire resistance and heat insulation than ordinary concrete, thanks to the tiny air bubbles that make them porous.

be willing to purchase this new type of concrete? Although Axel Eriksson's processes proved viable in industrial production, development took some time. In 1942 he established a facility in Stockholm to prefabricate concrete building components.

Axel Eriksson founded the company AB Betongindustri in Stockholm, where he served as managing director for 25 years. Use and production of aerated concrete expanded into many other countries as well.

A major advantage of aerated concrete over ordinary concrete was its superior thermal insulating quality. Aerated concrete was also fire-resistant, which made it suitable for use in housing. Swedish cities were bursting at the seams at that time, and many people felt a calling to build their own homes. Instead of mixing concrete on site and pouring it into moulds to set, housebuilders could now erect walls using precast components of aerated concrete, with no need for large cranes or cement mixer trucks.

A block of aerated concrete can be sawn in two with an ordinary saw. It is light enough to float in water, and nowadays it is available to purchase from ordinary builder's merchants. However, it is less durable, so it wouldn't be feasible to build a dome like the Pantheon has by using aerated concrete.

Then, in the 1950s, a serious issue emerged. The alum shale used in manufacturing aerated concrete was found to contain harmful traces of geological history. Minute quantities of uranium present in the shale were decaying and emitting radon, a radioactive gas. Radon gas is invisible, and little was known about its effects on the human body. It would take until the 1970s before the authorities started to act. Radon was found to cause lung cancer, and hundreds of thousands of homes had to be made safe. It was a public health emergency. Even now, one in six cases of lung cancer in Sweden is caused by radon. Some are due to aerated concrete, but radon is also emitted by Sweden's underlying bedrock.

Axel Eriksson, the inventor of aerated concrete, was not around to experience this distress. He passed away in 1961. Today, aerated concrete is produced without alum shale.

Worth preserving

NINNI KRONBERG AND POWDERED MILK

Milk – from cows, goats, sheep and other mammals – has been crucial throughout human history. It is easy to access, with a renewable supply, and contains important vitamins and nutrients. But there is a downside. If milk is not processed into another product (such as cheese or butter) with a longer shelf life, it quickly sours and goes bad.

Carnation "Magic Crystals" burst into fresh flavor
nonfat milk instantly-*for as little as 8¢ a quart!*

People consumed milk mainly in the form of cheese and butter rather than as a drink well into the 19th century. But with the advent of new technologies such as cream separation and pasteurisation and new forms of transport, milk became a vital commodity for urban dwellers – particularly in northern Europe. In Sweden and other countries, dairies became a major industry. Swedish adults as well as children drank milk, making Swedes' milk consumption among the highest in the world.

Even though Swedes were eager milk drinkers, Swedish dairies produced more milk than the people could consume. The question was how to make use of the surplus. That was when Johanna Kronberg, known as Ninni, entered the scene.

She was the daughter of a shipping company owner in Gävle and was privately educated by governesses. At the age of just 20, she married Erik Kronberg, a wholesale merchant. At first, she devoted herself to the household and her artistic interests, but during the First World War she got involved in the grain malthouse owned by her husband. Together, they developed and patented a method to produce yeast.

In the early 1920s, Ninni left her husband and moved in with her friend Gudrun Juel-Westrup on the Rydsgård estate in Skåne, southern Sweden. Working with Gudrun's husband Wilhelm Westrup, Ninni produced a new yeast preparation based on her earlier research. Westrup, who ran a dairy farm, was also interested in finding a way to preserve all the surplus milk he could not sell. That laid the groundwork for Ninni Kronberg's major invention – powdered milk. The first step was to remove the milkfat, to prevent the milk from going rancid. Then lactic acid was added and the skimmed milk was dehydrated in warm air. The result was powdered milk. When diluted with water, it was suitable for drinking, especially by young children, and for use in making bread, cured meats and other foods.

Ninni Kronberg obtained two patents on powdered milk: the first in 1934, and then for a further refinement in 1937. The Swedish military tried out the new product, with favourable results, so the Swedish government awarded her a 25,000-kronor grant to start manufacturing powdered milk on a commercial scale in Sweden, on condition that she establish a joint-stock company. The dairy co-op of the farmers' movement was not interested in getting involved, though. Instead, Axel Wenner-Gren, the founder of Electrolux, stepped in and founded the company Svensk Mjölkproduktion AB (known as SMP) in 1938. Ninni Kronberg did not join the company's board of directors, but she had a licensing agreement that generated royalties. The company planned to export powdered milk, but then the war intervened. Nevertheless, domestic demand for the product during the straitened war years generated healthy revenues.

After the war, SMP focused primarily on developing powdered milk products and baby food. Ninni Kronberg carried on her food science experiments and achieved new successes, including the creation of a new type of concentrated livestock feed. But she was also plagued by financial worries as a result of lawsuits concerning her patent for powdered milk. She died in 1949 at the age of 75. In 1963, SMP changed its name to Semper.

Children in the Netherlands drink milk made from powdered milk. It was provided as emergency aid after the Second World War.

An effective combination

SALAZOPYRIN (SULFASALAZINE)

Medical science is still searching for the causes of some of our most common diseases, including rheumatoid arthritis and inflammatory bowel disease. Even so, scientists have succeeded in developing effective medicines to treat these illnesses. Nanna Svartz was one such scientist. She combined two substances to create sulfasalazine, an anti-inflammatory, anti-bacterial drug that is still used all over the world 80 years after its launch.

Nanna Svartz grew up in Västerås, west of Stockholm, with educated parents. Deeply affected by the deaths of all four of her elder siblings due to tuberculosis, and fuelled by a strong inner drive and ambition, she applied to study medicine at the Karolinska Hospital in 1911 and was accepted. Following her studies, she secured a position at Stockholm's Seraphim Hospital working under Professor Israel Holmgren. Holmgren's interest in bowel disorders rubbed off

Rheumatoid arthritis is more common in women than men, but scientists do not know why. Nanna Svartz, who developed an effective drug to treat the condition, was appointed as Sweden's first female professor in 1937.

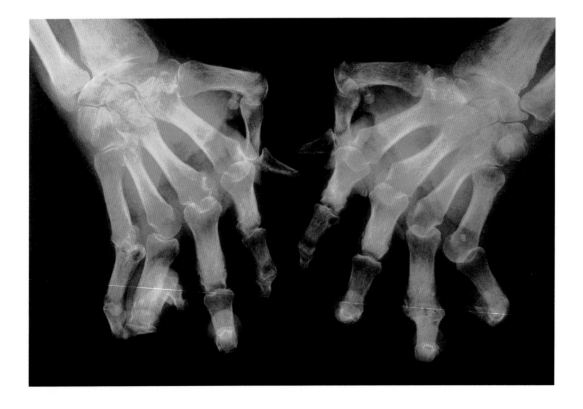

on Svartz, and she benefitted from his guidance and support. In those days, female scientists were few and far between. Her research focused on bowel microorganisms and the role of bacteria in the occurrence of bowel disease. But she didn't stop there. If bacteria were involved in bowel disease, she wondered, could they also be the cause of joint inflammation?

Rheumatoid arthritis is a common inflammatory disease that affects up to three times as many women as men. Its cause is still unknown. In the 1930s, scientists suspected an 'as yet unknown microbe'. While still a student, Nanna Svartz learned that Professor Gunnar Forssner had found 'bacteria-like formations' in joint fluid taken from patients with rheumatoid arthritis. Svartz isolated bacteria from rheumatoid arthritis patients and then injected the bacteria into live rabbits in the lab. At a medical conference in Lund in 1936, she displayed a live rabbit with swollen joints for the assembled specialists. After that presentation, no one doubted that bacteria played a key role in the disease.

Sulfanomides, also known as sulfa drugs, had proved to be effective at controlling bacteria in inflamed tissues. Meanwhile, salicylates were drugs that could provide quick pain relief for rheumatoid arthritis. 'Perhaps one should attempt a combination of sulfa and salicylates,' Svartz thought. She launched some experiments on her own and then obtained help from Erik Askelöf and Harry Willstaedt at Pharmacia, a pharmaceutical company.

In collaboration with Pharmacia, Nanna Svartz developed a drug that was brought to market in 1940 under the brand name Salazo-pyrin. It became the company's bestseller all the way into the 1960s. The drug is also sold under the generic name sulfasalazine. A few years earlier, Nanna Svartz had achieved the rank of full professor – the first woman to do so in a competitive application process. Some people had expressed doubts that 'a menopausal woman could handle such a senior position'. But plenty of people also treated her with great respect. Alongside her research, Svartz continued to treat prominent patients such as King Gustav V and Finland's Marshal Gustaf Mannerheim. She was a woman of high integrity, renowned for her capacity for hard work.

Easing the pain

LIDOCAINE (XYLOCAINE)

Patients sitting in the dentist's chair might wish to send a message of thanks to innovators Nils Löfgren and Bengt Lundqvist. After a quick injection of lidocaine, dentists can get to work with no fear of causing pain.

The story of how the anaesthetic lidocaine was developed will ring a bell with many chemistry students. Early in their studies, they are taught not to stick their nose in a test tube and definitely never to taste substances or – heaven forbid – test them on themselves. But two Swedish chemists, Nils Löfgren and Bengt Lundqvist, had other ideas.

In 1939, war had just broken out on the Continent. Meanwhile, a young chemist named Nils Löfgren had been toiling on a project at Stockholm University without much success. He was trying to synthesise a substance for use as a dental anaesthetic. His senior colleague Holger Erdtman had already given up and left their partnership. Löfgren didn't even have access to a proper laboratory. Instead, he was relegated to a windowless room in the basement, which also served as a bomb shelter.

Löfgren assembled a group of students in the bunker. One of them was Bengt Lundqvist, an enthusiastic young man. Lundqvist may well have contributed the most important factor in the group's progress – namely, the belief they would eventually succeed.

There was an urgent need for better anaesthetics. The preparations in use at the time were similar to cocaine and had a number of drawbacks. Their effects were short-lived, necessitating multiple injections. It was also difficult to get them to penetrate into the jaw.

One of the compounds Löfgren had used in his experiments with Erdtman was a substance that occurred naturally in certain species of grass. It numbed subjects' lips and tongue but was also highly toxic. The basement research team tried synthesising similar molecules. By adding a methyl group (a carbon atom bound to three hydrogen atoms) to the compound that had numbed their lips, they produced a candidate that seemed promising. They dubbed it lidocaine, or LL30 for short. Bengt Lundqvist's commitment to testing led him to test the substance on himself as well as on other scientists who served as trial subjects. 'We couldn't afford rabbits, so we had to test it on humans,' Lundqvist explained when he was asked why they didn't do any animal testing.

But Lundqvist's zeal for experimentation didn't stop there. He borrowed an anaesthesia textbook. Relying on the illustrations in the book alongside a mirror, he managed to self-administer a spinal anaesthetic. LL30 did the job, and the Swedish chemists' fortunes seemed to have taken a turn for the better.

By now it was 1943. Löfgren and Lundqvist offered the preparation for sale to Pharmacia, a major pharmaceutical firm at the time, but the company refused. In May of that year, the two scientists took the train to Södertälje, south of Stockholm, for a meeting at Astra, another large pharmaceutical company.

On the way there, Bengt Lundqvist suddenly remembered one of the problems dentists complained about with the leading dental anaesthetic: it couldn't penetrate into the jaw. So he grabbed the bag containing their new preparation and headed for the train's lavatory, where he injected some into his own mouth and awaited the results. Clearly everything worked as they had hoped, and the numbing effect was sufficiently long-lasting. Lundqvist sported a distinctly lopsided smile throughout their meeting at Astra.

An agreement was duly signed, and five years later Astra launched the compound on the market under the brand name Xylocaine. The product provided a boost for the company that would eventually grow into a global pharmaceutical corporation.

The Astra deal made Löfgren and Lundqvist millionaires. The story might have come to a neat conclusion at this point. Soon, though, dentists started reporting side effects such as swelling and skin irrita-

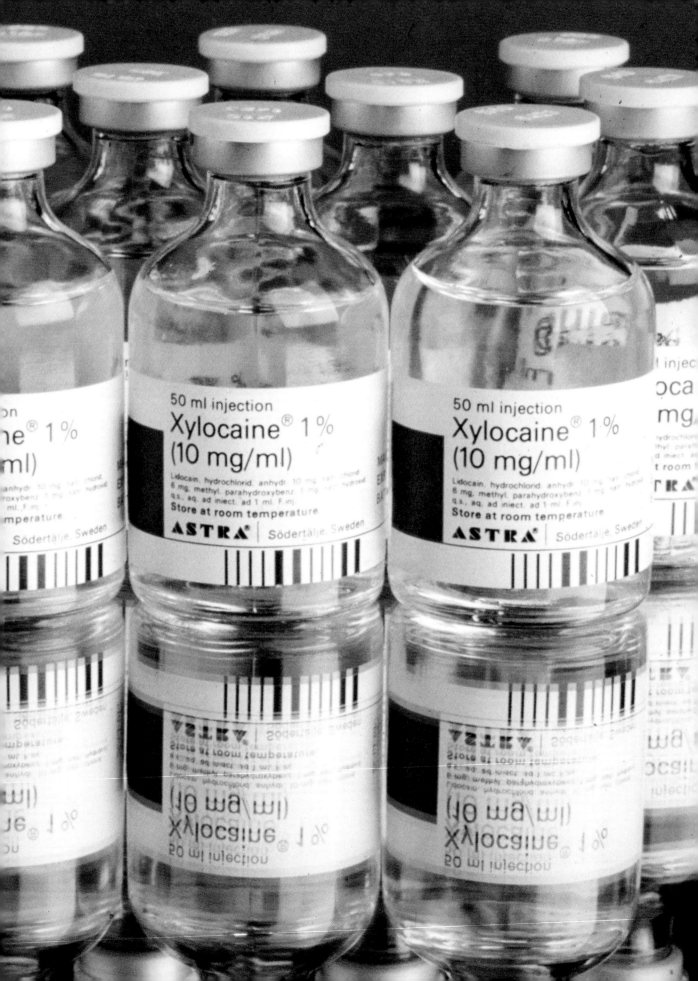

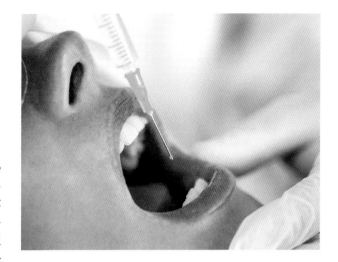

tion. The news hit Nils Löfgren hard, and he regarded it as a personal failure. Meanwhile, Bengt Lundqvist set about investigating the cause of the side effects. He found out which dentists had reported problems and visited their practices to see if anything about their methods differed from those of other dentists. He even visited some of the dentists incognito as a patient to analyse how they performed injections.

Lidocaine (xylocaine) is used as a local anaesthetic in many areas, particularly dentistry.

It turned out that the crucial factors were the type of syringe and the method of preparation. If the syringe was made of metal and the acidic substance was left in the syringe for some time before being used, some of the metal could dissolve and cause the side effects. Following this discovery, the dentists changed their routines and switched to glass syringes instead. The side effects stopped.

That was not enough to make Nils Löfgren feel better, though. He never found another research topic to immerse himself in, and he felt persecuted by the Swedish tax authorities. After relocating to the United States, his mental health worsened. He tried living in Switzerland, with no improvement. He was appointed to a professorship at Stockholm University in 1963 but resigned the following year. He suffered recurring episodes of depression and died in 1967.

As for the indefatigable Bengt Lundqvist, it turned out his reckless experimentation on himself had serious consequences. In 1952, not many years after their major breakthrough, Lundqvist fell down a flight of stairs in the chemistry department. His nerves had probably been damaged from all the injections. He suffered a concussion in the fall, which in turn led to a stroke. He died a short time later.

Lidocaine is still in widespread use all over the world. It is also the active ingredient in a cream for topical use. Among its many applications, doctors use it to numb children's skin in preparation for vaccination or general anaesthetic. A small tube of lidocaine cream is also indispensable in family medicine cabinets to provide quick relief from insect bites, cuts and burns.

Explosive safety

EJECTION SEAT

If an aircraft is plummeting to the ground, you need to bail out. The optimal way to do this is with a parachute. But first you need to get yourself and your parachute clear of the plane. With advances in fighter plane design during the Second World War, the aircraft speeds increased, thereby making it more difficult for the crew to safely leave the plane.

Sweden invested significantly in improving its air force during the Second World War. After scaling back its defences in the interwar period, the country's military capabilities – particularly in the air – lagged behind those of the major powers. The Swedish armed forces had been ill-prepared for the new air- and tank-based warfare in the war, but the country rushed to upgrade its armoury in the first half of the 1940s. Its efforts culminated in the 1950s, by which time Sweden had built up one of the world's most formidable air forces.

The need to develop an ejection seat was driven by the unconventional design of the Saab J 21 fighter plane, with the engine and propeller fitted right behind the pilot. In the last years of the war, Swedish ejection systems were tested, using the Saab 17 reconnaissance dive bomber as a platform. Mass production began in 1945 when an ejection seat was fitted as standard in the Saab J 21 fighter. The first operational use of ejection seats occurred in 1946, when two J 21 aircraft collided in mid-air during an exercise off Sweden's west coast near Gothenburg. Both pilots survived, thanks to their ejection seats.

As Second Lieutenant Bengt Järkenstedt, one of the pilots involved, later described the episode: 'I pulled my goggles down from my forehead. My oxygen mask was already in place… Right hand on the ejector lever. Close your eyes and pull the lever towards you. I might have lost consciousness momentarily, but when I opened my eyes, I found myself in mid-air with the seat behind me, around 10 metres above the aircraft.' Järkenstedt suffered no ill effects from ejecting and was back on duty two days later.

During the war, Germany had also developed various methods for pilots to exit themselves from emergencies in the air. In the early 1940s, test models of the turbojet-powered Heinkel He 280 fighter aircraft were equipped with an ejection seat that was propelled by

When Saab was designing the J 21 fighter plane in the 1940s, it placed the propeller behind the engine in a pusher configuration to make room for guns in the aircraft's nose. That created a danger for the pilot of getting caught in the rotating propeller if he bailed out with a parachute. The solution was an ejection seat, powered by an explosive charge that ejected the pilot clear of the propeller.

compressed air. The Swedish version was fired by gunpowder rather than compressed air.

Saab did not manage to secure a patent on its ejection seat. Instead, Martin-Baker, a British aviation equipment manufacturer, patented its own model and went on to become a leading global flight safety firm. Modern ejection seats rely on rocket propulsion to eject the pilot well clear of a jet plane travelling at high speed, standing on the ground, or in any flight condition in between.

Stacked milk

RAUSING, WALLENBERG AND TETRA PAK

Soon after the First World War, Ruben Rausing, a 24-year-old economics student, was awarded a scholarship to study at Columbia University in New York. In the United States, the young man encountered a new phenomenon: self-service stores where customers selected their own items off the shelf for purchase. Rausing realised that in the future, vast quantities of packaging would be required to transport and sell groceries that had previously been sold in bulk from large jars, crates and barrels.

After his return to Sweden, Rausing teamed up with Erik Åkerlund, a newspaper owner, to establish the company Åkerlund & Rausing. They planned to develop new packaging concepts. While dry goods were relatively easy to package for retail sale, liquid foods were much more difficult. Perhaps the biggest challenge was milk. It sold in huge quantities but was highly perishable, with implications for food safety and shelf life.

In those days, Swedes bought their milk from special shops. Milk merchants did not carry many other types of products because they were not permitted to sell foodstuffs that could taint the milk with hazardous bacteria – in particular meat and vegetables grown in the soil. Milk was delivered fresh every morning, and customers brought their own jugs and containers to take the milk home in, though some was also sold in bottles. The small-scale operations and lack of refrigeration meant that almost every city block had its own dairy shop. In the 1930s, there were nearly 2,000 shops selling milk in Stockholm alone.

Rausing's idea was to distribute milk in airtight paper containers. But how could he make it work? At the end of the Second World War, he asked his young lab assistant Erik Wallenberg to work on the problem. Wallenberg came up with a four-sided, pyramid-shaped paper container that could be folded from a single piece of paper – a tetrahedron. The idea was to roll the paper into a tube. The tube was filled with milk, then the ends were sealed and the package was shaped into a pyramid.

Rausing took out a patent on the concept in 1944. But the problem had only been solved in theory. In order to put their idea into practice,

The original Tetra Pak concept: flat paper packaging transformed into a tetrahedron.

Fig 1

Fig 2

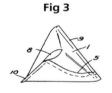

Fig 3

Fig 4

they needed suitable materials and high-capacity packaging machinery. Over the next few years, Åkerlund & Rausing – which changed its name to Tetra Pak in 1950 – worked on making the tetrahedron package commercially viable.

A breakthrough came when Rausing – inspired by his wife Elisabeth – hit upon the idea to pour a continuous stream of milk into a tube and then crimp the tube off into individual packs, as Erik Wallenberg had described. Another piece of the puzzle came when they heard that America's plastics industry had developed a material called polyethylene, which could be used on the inside of the tetrahedrons to prevent leaks. But in order to scale up production, they still needed a machine capable of filling plastic-laminated paper tubes with milk, cutting them into individual pyramids and sealing the packets.

On 18 May 1951, everything seemed to be in place. Members of the press were invited to a demonstration in Lund, followed by dinner at the Grand Hotel. But there was a problem. The sealing process had not been perfected yet, and some of the packages leaked.

So the journalists were not allowed to see the automatic packing equipment that placed the pyramids in the hexagonal metal baskets for distribution. Instead, the packets were whisked off the production line through a hole in the wall and then emerged from the other side in their baskets. Behind the wall stood two packers who set the incoming packets aside and replaced them with baskets that had previously been filled with packets guaranteed to be sealed. The journalists were impressed, and no one asked any probing questions.

The first 20 years were tough, with many production problems and customer complaints. Tetra Pak's major breakthrough came in the form of an aseptic container called Tetra Brik Aseptic. It was easy to fill at dairies, with a rectangular shape that was more consumer-friendly than the original pyramid. Nowadays these cartons are filled with many things besides milk.

Today, Tetra Pak has a presence in over 160 countries, with around 25,000 employees and an annual turnover of more than 11 billion euros.

The original Tetra Pak package shape, the tetrahedron, is seldom used today. Other, more retailer- and refrigerator-friendly shapes are used instead.

Erik Wallenberg received belated recognition for his contribution in 1991, when he was awarded the Royal Swedish Academy of Engineering Sciences' Great Gold Medal 'for his idea and development of the Tetra Pak packaging system'.

Identify yourself
NATIONAL IDENTIFICATION NUMBER

There's really nothing unique about a country allocating personal ID numbers to its citizens. As the modern nation state developed in the 20th century and citizens had more dealings with government authorities, many countries introduced some sort of identification number system to supplement people's names, which were neither unique nor sufficient for identification purposes.

In the United States, Social Security numbers were introduced under President Franklin D. Roosevelt's New Deal programme in the 1930s, a decade before Sweden's system came about. At first, these numbers were mainly used in connection with pensions and other welfare benefits, but their use has expanded into other areas, particularly tax administration. The UK, Austria, Canada and other countries have similar systems. Germany forbids the use of a single ID number to identify each citizen for all purposes, probably for historical reasons. Instead, people there have different numbers in the social insurance, pension and tax systems. It helps to preserve privacy, but all the numbers are hard to remember.

Nevertheless, Sweden was the first country to introduce personal ID numbers based on citizens' date of birth followed by a short numerical code. The move was prompted by the introduction of 'pay-as-you-earn' taxation, where individuals' income tax is deducted at source instead of being paid later on. The new ID numbers had other advantages too. During the Second World War, the old population register had proved to be unwieldy. For example, young men reporting for mandatory military service had a hard time verifying their identity when they were far away from the office of the parish where they were born. Under the old system, people were either known locally or produced some sort of document such as a letter addressed and posted to them to verify their identity at the post office, bank or other venue. If someone was unavailable to vote in their home municipality, they would write a letter of proxy for their spouse or relative, which was not entirely fraud-proof.

What makes Swedish national ID numbers (known as 'person numbers') unique is that, unlike the randomness of American Social Security numbers, they have a personal connection to the bearer –

plus, they are easy to remember. The format is YYMMDD-XXXX. Everyone remembers their date of birth, so they just have to memorise the last few digits. That code at the end is cleverly constructed. Initially, it was a three-digit number between 000 and 999, with even numbers for females and odd numbers for males. Then, in 1968, a fourth digit was added to the end as a check digit based on the other nine digits. The check digit is calculated using an algorithm, which makes it difficult for anyone to make up a fake ID number if they haven't gone to the trouble of learning that complicated algorithm.

The ease of remembering Swedish ID numbers, combined with the difficulty of faking them, makes the numbers convenient to use in many contexts. Add to that Sweden's efficient population registry that goes back to the 18th century and modern BankID digital technology for electronic transactions, and the country has a system that makes it easy for citizens to prove their identity in dealings with public authorities and all sorts of transactions in daily life. This makes sense financially by reducing transaction costs with banks, businesses and other entities. Swedish ID numbers also make voting and elections very secure. Other countries – including Norway, Denmark, Finland and France – have followed Sweden's model for their own national ID numbers, with some variations.

Swedish ID numbers have also streamlined new digital technologies for identification and financial transaction in comparison to many other countries. Sweden was not the first to introduce electronic identification, but the BankID system is much easier to use because it's based on personal ID numbers, which everyone knows by heart. As a result, nearly everyone has the app for Swish, Sweden's e-payment system, on their phone. Swish lets people send instant payments to other people by phone, secured by Mobile BankID. This, along with widespread use of debit and credit cards, has made Sweden a virtually cash-free country.

Sucking it up

WETTEX ABSORBING CLOTH

Not every Swedish innovation is something we use every day. The story of Wettex cleaning cloths starts at home with Curt Lindquist, an engineer who got tired of using cloths that weren't up to the job. He wanted something absorbent that could wipe up dirt and spills in the kitchen.

The idea came to him at work. Lindquist was the manager of a factory that manufactured household sponges and sausage casings from cellulose. Cellulose is a substance that forms plant cell walls. It is highly absorbent and also happens to be the most abundant organic polymer in the world. Nowadays when we hear about replacing fossil fuels and plastics with biomaterials, cellulose is the most likely replacement. The cellulose fibres Curt Lindquist started to experiment with were obtained from wood.

Synthetic household sponges, which Lindquist already held a patent on, were highly absorbent. What if a cloth could be made from the same material? One day, he took some sponges home from work. Soon, his whole family was involved in the project. The children put the sponges through a meat grinder to produce a sticky mass, which was then rolled out into a thin sheet and dried. Unfortunately, it did not hold together. Later, Lindquist hit upon the idea to incorporate some cotton fibres. Then the material started to resemble a cleaning cloth when it was damp.

It turned out that Curt Lindquist and his helpful family had managed to create a material that could absorb 15 times its own weight in water. His wife Margareta coined the name Wettex by combining the English words *wet* and *textile*.

In 1949, Lindquist's company launched this revolutionary new cleaning cloth made from natural, biodegradable material. The cloths were manufactured in the Norrköping factory – where they are still produced today. Newer versions have come along since then, but all have adhered to Lindquist's concept. For optimal effectiveness, the cloth should be dampened and then wrung out before use. If it gets dirty, it can be machine-washed at 60 degrees Celsius and reused. At the end of its useful life, the cloth can be composted.

Europe is the main market for Wettex cloths, but they are sold all over the world. They have even been to outer space. In the 1960s, NASA got wind of the amazing new cloths and wanted to see if the absorbent material would work as insulation in spacecraft. It took some effort for Curt Lindquist to achieve the right shade of grey to meet NASA's specifications, but then it was not long before he received official word that his cloth was in space. The cloth was a bit too flammable for NASA's liking, though, so Sweden's Wettex material made just the one journey beyond the Earth's atmosphere.

A Wettex cleaning cloth, made from cellulose, can absorb 15 times its own weight in water.

Saving lives every day

VENTILATOR

Imagine being unable to breathe … During the coronavirus pandemic that fear was realised for unprecedented numbers of people. Ventilators – another Swedish innovation – played a crucial role in saving lives.

People suffered breathing difficulties during previous epidemics as well. When a polio epidemic broke out in the late 1940s, the main treatment available was the iron lung. It resembled a large tin can that enclosed the patient's entire body, with just their head sticking out through a rubber collar. The iron lung worked by alternating high and low pressure around the patient's body, helping them to inhale and exhale. Even so, many patients died.

When Carl Gunnar Engström qualified as a doctor in 1941, he took up a post to treat infectious diseases at Stockholm's isolation hospital. If he had contented himself with that role, the modern ventilator would never have come about. Fortunately, Engström took on an extra job with the Swedish Air Force, examining test pilots who flew near the sound barrier.

Supersonic flight was in its infancy in the late 1940s. Saab, the Swedish engineering and manufacturing company, had started developing a fighter plane that could reach such speeds. A Saab 32 Lansen exceeded the sound barrier for the first time in 1953.

Engström was interested in the effects of such extreme forces on the levels of various gases in pilots' blood, so he conducted a series of tests.

Engström quickly noticed a similarity between his patients and the supersonic pilots. Too much carbon dioxide remained in the patients' blood. Because it was not possible to check how much air patients were getting inside the iron lung, doctors could not monitor their oxygen and carbon dioxide levels. Engström developed an air pump that could regulate the air in a patient's lungs by means of an airtight tube in their trachea. In July 1950, his first prototype was ready. The first volume-controlled artificial ventilator went into production the following year. In addition to helping many polio patients, the device was of great benefit in operating theatres.

In 1963, Carl Gunnar Engström received his PhD on the basis of his invention. Further improvements were made as the device spread round the world.

The original Engström ventilator was large and bulky, but it represented a revolution in healthcare by pumping air into patients' lungs. It was widely used in a polio epidemic in the 1950s.

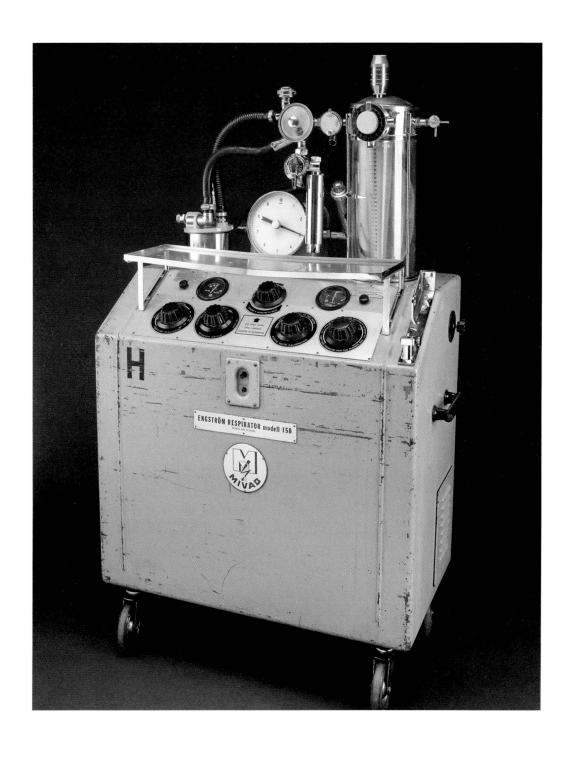

The crucial breakthrough is credited to a Swedish medical student, Björn Jonson, who in turn got the idea for a flow regulator from his lecturer Sven Ingelstedt in 1964. Ingelstedt kept a collection of unsolved problems in a folder labelled 'Only God and I know'. Ingelstedt's self-confidence was as great as his generosity towards others. He had dismissed earlier attempts to create a functional flow regulator, saying, 'You cannot regulate the flow'. But when Björn Jonson, who had also identified the issue of regulating the timing and rate at which air was delivered to patients, asked, 'If I figure out how to regulate it, can we build a ventilator?' Ingelstedt was quick to reply, 'Absolutely!'

That was the first step along the path to the modern ventilators we have today. The problem was that Jonson had no access to a laboratory and no knowledge of how to build medical equipment. But he knew where he could get help. Soon he made friends with skilled technicians at the hospital in Lund. They helped him to grind, polish and drill glass and metal components. When Jonson nearly caused a disaster in the hospital's workshop, he was banned from the facility. Then Håkan Westling, professor of clinical physiology, purchased a lathe and a milling machine, which they set up in a broom cupboard, under the hospital management's radar. Jonson used the equipment to assemble some functioning flow regulators. Working with Sven Gunnar Olsson, an engineer, he also constructed a new type of ventilator. It was silent and weighed just 4 kilograms (8.8 lb), a fraction of Engström's bulky model. Crucially, it was far more versatile. It allowed patients some control over their breathing. Björn Jonson applied for a patent on his ventilator. The following day, he headed to Elema-Schönander, a medical technology company that would later be acquired by Siemens.

The company invested significant resources in the device and gave Jonson and Olsson, working with anaesthetist Lars Nordström, the freedom to continue refining their ideas. Their new ventilator featured electronic flow and pressure gauges, and they soon added a carbon dioxide gauge. As a physiologist, Jonson knew that the diagnostics was as important as providing air flow to the patient. When their ServoVentilator was launched 1971, it quickly became a global leader. Updated versions are still manufactured by Getinge today.

The modern ServoVentilator functions as both breathing support and diagnostic instrument. When it was launched in 1971, it formed the basis of intensive care, an entirely new concept at the time.

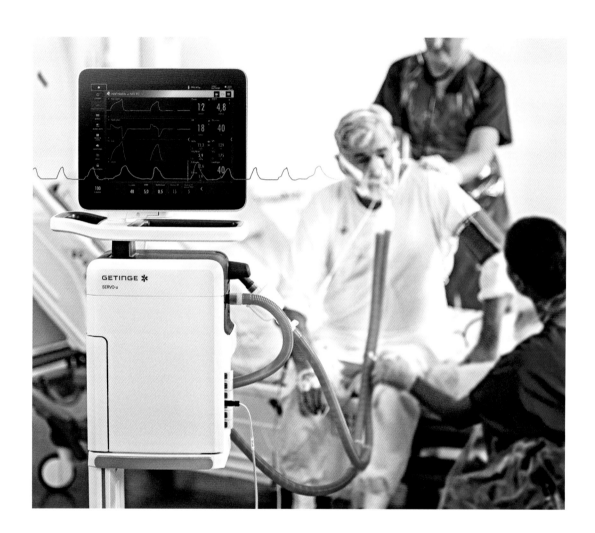

To view the unseen
ECHOCARDIOGRAPHY AND ULTRASOUND

Aheartbeat, the extent of a malignant tumour, or a foetus in its mother's womb. Ultrasound lets us see inside the body. The very first ultrasound examination was performed on a heart patient in Lund in 1953.

As a medical student in Lund in the 1930s, Inge Edler had two great interests: anatomy and magic. He would go on to become one of Sweden's most respected cardiologists – and a skilled magician. With props ordered specially from Germany, he performed tricks that dazz-led his friends. The medical innovation he introduced would bring about similar reactions.

In the early 1950s, significant advances were made in open-heart surgery, enabling surgeons to correct previously inoperable heart defects. But surgery required a precise diagnosis. Surgeons wanted a clear picture of a patient's heart before picking up a scalpel. Inge Edler, now chief physician at Lund University Hospital, approached Hellmuth Hertz, then an assistant in the university's physics department, and asked for some advice. As it turned out, Edler couldn't have chosen a better person to ask. Their idea was inspired by echo sounding, a technology used by commercial fishermen to locate schools of fish in the sea. Could the same type of high-frequency sound waves be directed at a patient's chest to generate an image of their heart?

Hertz is a name to be reckoned with in physics. Hellmuth Hertz was the son of the Nobel laureate Gustav Hertz, whose uncle Heinrich Hertz was the first person to prove the existence of electromagnetic waves. He lent his name to the unit of frequency, the Hertz (Hz), which is still in use today.

Edler had no trouble getting Hertz on board to help with the challenges of coronary diagnostics. After ruling out Edler's initial idea of using radar, Hertz suggested that they could try ultrasound, which was in its infancy at that time. Hertz had heard that Kockums shipyard in nearby Malmö was using ultrasound to inspect welding seams. He managed to borrow a set of equipment from Siemens. They were ready to start experimenting.

The idea of Edler and Hertz was to aim high-frequency sound waves at the patient's chest. Then a detector captured the echo reflected from

Ultrasound is used to examine a patient's carotid artery for fatty deposits that can block blood flow to the brain and increase the risk of stroke and dementia.

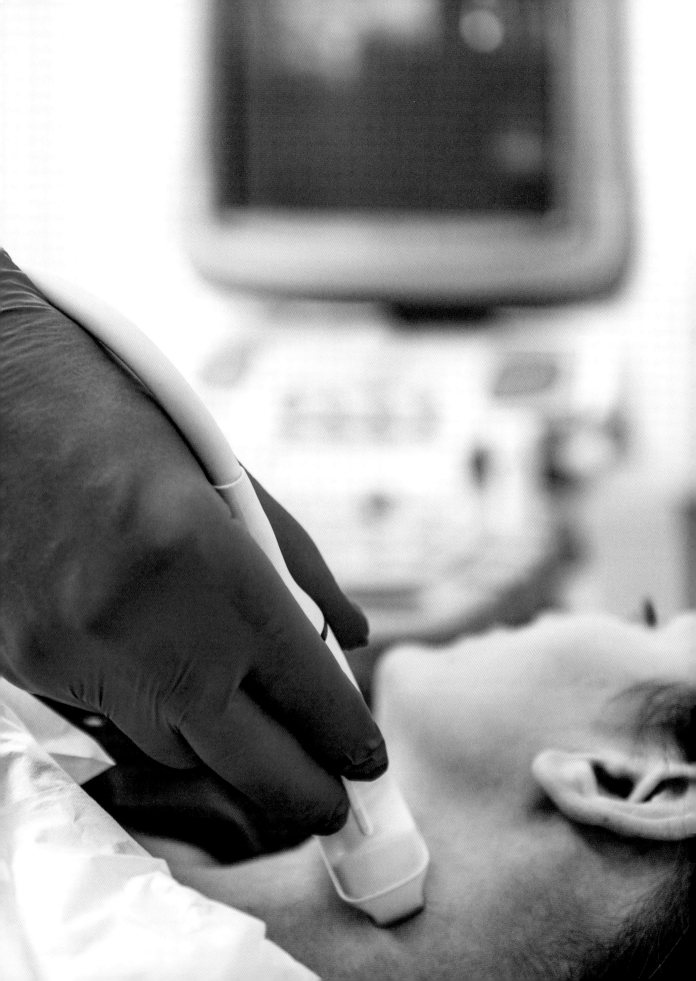

a heart valve or the heart wall to produce an image of the various parts of the heart. The longer it took for the signal to return, the greater the distance – the same principle as in echo sounding. Ultrasound waves have a frequency of over 20,000 Hz, which is outside human hearing range (between 20 and 20,000 Hz).

Edler and Hertz were their own first test subjects. The equipment worked, though it was large and cumbersome. By 29 October 1953, they were ready to place their ultrasound detector on a real heart patient for the first time. While Inge Edler looked after the patient, Hellmuth Hertz stood nearby and adjusted the amplitude on the os-cilloscope screen.

This technique became known as pulse echo imaging. It spread rapidly around the world. Further refinements were added along the way. The first practical applications were developed in the UK and the United States. Nowadays it is possible to monitor the heart's ac-tion on screen in real time, observe blood flow and diagnose the con-dition of tissues. Echocardiography has become a routine diagnostic technique, along with electrocardiography. Ultrasound is also used to examine other organs and tissues in the body, such as diagnosing ma-lignant tumours and monitoring fatty deposits in the carotid artery.

In the early 1960s, ultrasound was used on a pregnant woman for the first time. Today, expectant parents can take home a photo from their regular ultrasound scans – or why not make a video of the new family member-to-be? Best of all, it's not magic at all, but pure science.

Many people know about ultrasound from prenatal scans, when they get to see their unborn child for the first time.

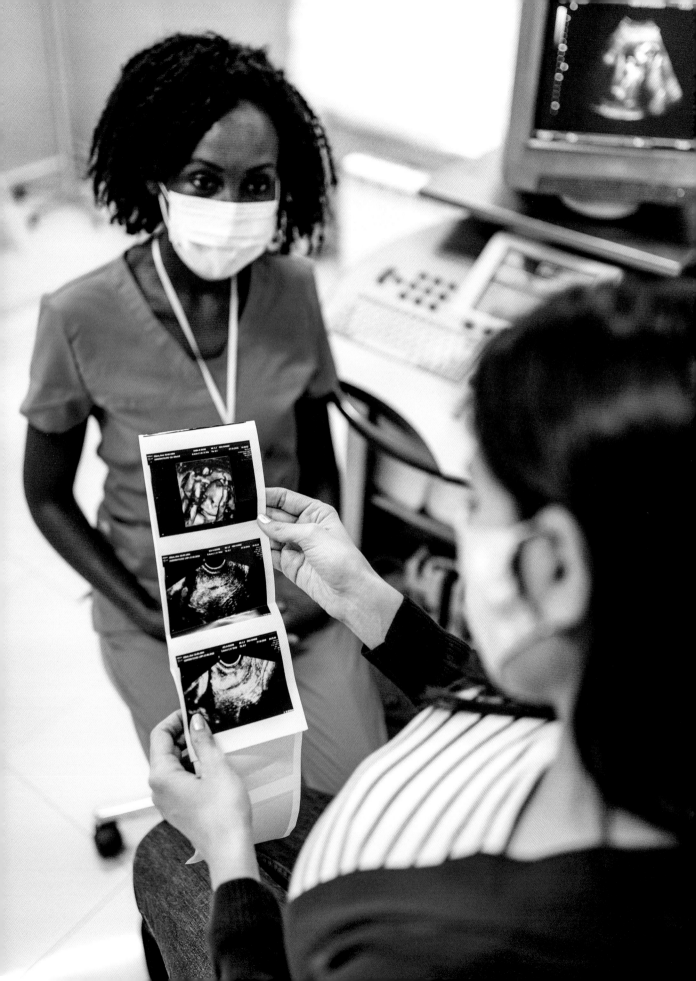

Self-assembly

IKEA AND FLATPACKS

People all over the world have got used to furnishing their homes with furniture that comes in parts they assemble themselves according to illustrated instructions with no words. The flat cardboard boxes and pictures of a cartoon figure with an Allen key have become global pop-culture references – from odd-sounding product names containing 'funny' Nordic letters like Å, Ä and Ö to cartoons depicting Donald Trump's Mexican border wall as a set of components from IKEA.

According to IKEA legend, the cardboard flatpacks came about in 1956, when the company's founder Ingvar Kamprad and designer Gillis Lundgren removed the legs from a 'Lövet' table in order to fit it into the boot of a car. Furniture had been sold in ready-to-assemble parts before that, though. Some furniture manufacturers supplied their products to retailers as sets, which the retailers had to assemble on their premises. And in 1944 the Swedish furniture designer Elias Svedberg, working with Lena Larsson and Erik Wørts, created chairs and a table that came flatpacked for customers to assemble themselves, though that was more of an experiment.

Nevertheless, it was Ingvar Kamprad who realised the vast potential of flatpacks to streamline furniture supply chains. When he and Gillis Lundgren unscrewed the legs from the 'Lövet' table, Kamprad was 30 years old and had been running a mail-order business since the age of 17. He had named the company after his initials and his hometown: Ingvar Kamprad from Elmtaryd in the Agunnaryd parish in Småland. He started out selling ballpoint pens, wallets, nylon stockings and whatever else the enterprising young man could get hold of.

In 1947, he added furniture to his product range. Living standards were rising in Sweden, which had avoided the destruction of the Second World War. More and more young people were getting married and setting up house together. Kamprad saw there was a market for inexpensive beds, sofas, armchairs, tables and other furniture a new household needed. He was also aware that Scandinavian interior design had gone from heavy, dark, cluttered looks to lighter, more functional aesthetics.

With his mail-order business, Kamprad could reach a far larger customer base than local furniture shops. But sending tables, chairs,

IKEA's first storage facility in the hamlet of Elmtaryd, located in Småland's Agunnaryd parish, in 1948. The letters in IKEA stand for Ingvar Kamprad, Elmtaryd, Agunnaryd.

bookcases and other bulky items through the post was expensive and awkward. Regardless of how the idea came about, IKEA's true breakthrough came with the advent of flatpacks. In 1958, Kamprad expanded the exhibition room he had opened in Älmhult into a fully fledged furniture store.

At first, IKEA did not enjoy the best of reputations. Other furniture manufacturers boycotted Kamprad, believing him to engage in unfair competition. Customers liked the low prices but buying furniture by mail order was hardly the way to impress one's family and friends. But for Ingvar Kamprad, it wasn't just about keeping prices down. He was convinced it was possible to combine quality with quantity in the 20th-century modernist design tradition. He engaged innovative designers. It is no coincidence that Sweden's second IKEA store, located on Kungens Kurva in southern Stockholm, was inspired by New York's Guggenheim Museum.

Today, IKEA endeavours to present itself as a product of Sweden's *folkhemmet* – the values that shaped the post-war nation into the 'people's home'. That image is of an environmentally aware company that gives citizens equal access to home furnishings that are both practical and tasteful. That story may be somewhat mythologised, but with more than 400 stores in 64 markets and an annual turnover of 40 billion euros, IKEA has proved that flatpacks do the job.

All of IKEA's 400 stores around the world use the same simple system. After strolling through the showrooms, customers enter the warehouse and pick up their flatpack furniture themselves. Over 750 million customers visit IKEA stores every year.

Buckle up

THE SEAT BELT

The number of people who die in traffic accidents in Sweden has gone down drastically in the past 50 years, from 1,307 people in 1970 to 210 in 2021. The reduction is actually even greater than the statistics indicate, because the country's population and the number of vehicles increased during that period.

There are several reasons for the reduction in fatalities, including better roads and speed limits. But a large proportion of lives were saved as a result of seat belts. Securing drivers inside vehicles is not a specifically Swedish idea, but Swedish innovators have made significant improvements to seat belt technology.

Seat belts were first used in the 19th century in early gliders to prevent pilots falling out. When commercial passenger air travel began in the 1930s, airlines introduced seat belts for passengers as well as crew. The car-driving public resisted using seat belts for a long time, though. Nash, an American automaker, introduced seat belts in its cars in 1949, but most customers demanded the belts be removed. In 1955, Ford offered seat belts as an optional extra in its cars, but only 2 per cent of buyers opted to have them installed.

Over the next decades, Swedish inventors and companies played a crucial role in improving seat belt technology. Surprisingly, Sweden's state-owned power company Vattenfall took up the cause. Vattenfall was losing a frightening number of its employees as they drove along narrow, bumpy roads in northern Sweden from one power station to another. The company tasked two engineers – Bengt Odelgard and Per-Olof Weman – with developing a seat belt. They came up with a diagonal design. Earlier belts were worn across the lap. Starting in 1956, 'Vattenfall-type seat belts' were installed in the company's vehicles.

Around the same time, Lennart Lindblad, an ironmonger, and his brother Stig, who had a car repair workshop, were developing their own seat belt. After the death of a friend in a car accident, Lennart purchased a harness and planned to strap himself into his car on his next motoring holiday. But the harness turned out to be flimsy, so he fabricated his own from a nylon strap that could withstand a load of 400 kilograms (880 lb). He also read about Vattenfall seat belts in the

Most people were not keen on wearing seat belts at first. Demonstrations to educate drivers and passengers were given all over Sweden. This is one such event in Gothenburg in 1955.

newspaper. Lennart sought permission to copy the idea, and he and his brother Stig began constructing their own seat belts. From his hardware store, Lennart used a buckle that was meant for use on livestock collars. His wife and mother helped out, working in the attic to sew the buckles on. Production expanded rapidly into a large business that sold seat belts under the brand name Autoliv to a number of European car manufacturers. Today, Autoliv is a global corporation with some 68,000 employees.

The Lindblad brothers also attracted interest from Volvo. In the late 1950s, Nils Bohlin worked as an engineer in Volvo's safety division. He is often credited as the inventor of the three-point seat belt, but in fact he refined an existing belt used in American aeroplanes. Bohlin started from the existing patented design and created a number of refinements for use in cars and trucks, resulting in a new patent.

The three-point seat belt combined the diagonal belt and the lap belt – hence the three points – resulting in much improved safety. The three-point belt was included as standard in Volvo cars for the Nordic market from 1959. Both Volvo and Saab realised they could make safety a unique selling point for their vehicles in the North American market. Seat belt use started to increase in the United States, and soon American automakers followed the Swedish car companies' lead.

The next major improvement was the self-locking retractor belt, developed in the early 1960s by a helicopter engineer named Hans Karlsson in his spare time while he was employed by Lamco, a Swedish mining company, in Liberia. In 1967, he sold his invention to Autoliv, which noticed that the belt's rolling action made seat belts more comfortable to wear.

There is no question that seat belts save lives. They are now required by law in all EU countries, but they still need to be simple and convenient to encourage people to wear them.

Volvo advertisement from the 1950s, featuring a three-point seat belt.

The heart of the matter

THE PACEMAKER

The heart is our most amazing muscle. Did you know that a human heart beats 30 million times each year? If this rhythmic pumping stops, a person will die within just a few minutes. Yet some three million men and women with heart problems are living normal lives today with the help of devices that regulate heart contractions – known as pacemakers.

The first pacemaker was implanted in a living person on 8 October 1958. That life-giving device was the brainchild of Rune Elmqvist, a doctor and engineer.

Two other men deserve a mention in connection with this event: Professor Åke Svenning of Karolinska Hospital was the surgeon wielding the scalpel, and Arne Larsson was the patient on the operating table. Larsson was 43 years old and suffered from a heart arrhythmia that caused him to faint up to 30 times a day.

The heart has always been a source of fascination. Three and a half millennia ago, the ancient Egyptians knew about the heart, pulse and blood vessels. In the fourth century BCE the Greek physician Hippocrates, considered the father of medicine, described the heart as a muscle with two chambers and valves.

Still the biggest mystery remained unsolved. How does this muscle manage to keep beating in rhythm?

Scientists in the Age of Enlightenment began to get closer to an answer when they began working with electricity, a recent discovery, in attempts to treat severe disorders such as epilepsy and paralysis. One of the pioneers in this area was Carl von Linné (also known as Linnaeus), a Swedish botanist and physician.

In the late 18th century, a Danish veterinarian named P. C. Abildgaard conducted a series of bold experiments to study the heart. His subjects were mainly chickens, as well as some horses. Using electric shocks, he managed to make the animals' hearts stop – and then start beating again. His findings helped to increase hopes of finding medical applications for electricity. But it was not until the early 20th century before people started using electricity in effective treatments for coronary ailments.

One of Rune Elmqvist's very first pacemakers. He managed to make it as small as a matchbox. It had to be small enough to be implanted in patients. Elmqvist's adoption of another amazing innovation from the United States, the transistor, made it possible.

In 1932 Albert Hyman, an American doctor, developed a device that could restart a heart by means of electrodes. Unfortunately, the device weighed over 7 kilograms (15 lb) and had to be hand-cranked to recharge every six minutes, making it both impractical and hazardous. Hyman ended up abandoning his experiments.

Twenty years later, another American, Paul Zoll, made an attempt. He managed to produce a pacemaker that was capable of stimulating the heart to maintain its proper rhythm, but it was large and unwieldy, with numerous electrodes that had to be placed on the patient's chest. Treatment with this device, which had to be done in hospital, was unpleasant and painful.

Rune Elmqvist had qualified as a doctor in Lund, but with the exception of a brief period as a ship's doctor, he never practised medicine. His real passion was engineering. At the age of 21 he had invented an instant pH meter, a device for measuring acidity. A few years later he set up his own technical workshop, where he developed and manufactured a new portable, multichannel type of ECG device.

In 1940, Elmqvist's company merged with another company that later became Siemens-Elema. Elmqvist was in charge of product development, and new inventions were not slow in coming. His innovations included the mingograph, a form of inkjet printer that was used for many years to record ECG results as a needle moved across a strip of paper – the first such device that permitted the use of multiple sensors.

Elmqvist also had the good fortune of knowing Dr. Åke Svenning, a surgeon. The two men worked together for many years at the medical device manufacturer Siemens-Elema, coming up with a string of successes that started when Elmqvist got wind of a revolutionary new technology for amplifying electrical signals – the transistor. Based on new semiconductors and invented in 1947 by a group of American engineers who were later awarded a Nobel Prize, the transistor could be used instead of vacuum tubes in computers and other electronic devices. The transistor meant these devices could be made smaller, more reliable and faster, with reduced energy consumption. A computer that previously would have taken up an entire room could fit on a desktop. Elmqvist thought about the possibilities. He tested

Today, doctors can implant a pacemaker under local anaesthesia in about an hour. Electrodes leading from the pacemaker are connected to the heart via a vein.

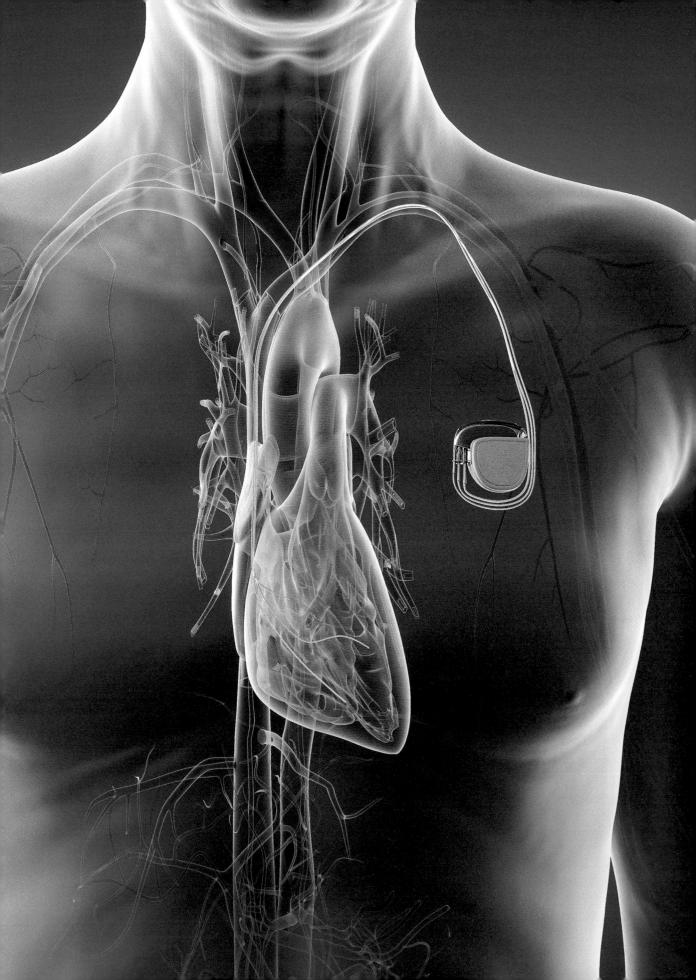

his ideas on his colleague Dr. Svenning. What if they could make a pacemaker small enough to be implanted inside a patient's body?

They decided to give it a try. Rune Elmqvist ordered some of the new transistor chips from the United States. He constructed a signal generator he could connect to flexible electrodes, powered by a long-life battery. The first prototype could maintain a frequency of 72 beats per minute. Its components were soldered together in a coffee cup!

After a few weeks of intense experimentation, Elmqvist's pacemaker was ready, sealed inside a plastic case the size of a matchbox. Once implanted in the body, the pacemaker would send brief electrical shocks via an electrode to the upper right heart chamber. These impulses could make the heart work normally by causing the heart muscle to contract, thereby pumping blood around the circulatory system. In people with healthy hearts, their pulse is regulated by the heart's sinus node, which emits regular electrical signals. Rune Elmqvist was hopeful that his new device would take the place of the cumbersome hospital equipment that had previously been called a pacemaker.

In October 1958, Arne Larsson was under anaesthetic on the operating table. His heart problems had started following a serious case of food poisoning, probably caused by eating bad oysters at a restaurant. He got some help for his frequent fainting spells that resulted from the food poisoning thanks to his alert secretary, who would thump him on the back – she sometimes also gave him a glass of whisky to stimulate his circulation. But that was not a long-term solution.

Now Åke Svenning was about to implant the brand-new invention in Larsson's chest. Fortunately, Rune Elmqvist had produced two of the pacemakers, because the first one stopped after three hours. But with the second pacemaker in place, Larsson's heart beat steadily for a full week. Later versions were more reliable. Throughout the rest of his life, Arne Larsson had to have his pacemaker replaced 26 times. He lived to the age of 86 and actually outlived both Svenning and Elmqvist.

A modern pacemaker functions in essentially the same way as Elmqvist's first model. Three million people with heart problems are able to live well today, thanks to their pacemakers.

Today's pacemakers work basically the same way as Rune Elm-qvist's initial model. They regulate the heartbeat by sending electrical signals directly into the heart. Implantation is done under local anaesthetic, and the pacemaker can be modified and adjusted for each patient later, with no additional surgery. A modern pacemaker will last between seven and 13 years and can even communicate with hospital computer systems, so the patient's doctor will know if anything is not right.

Neither Rune Elmqvist nor Åke Svenning believed the pacemaker would make much of an impact, so they never bothered to register a patent for it.

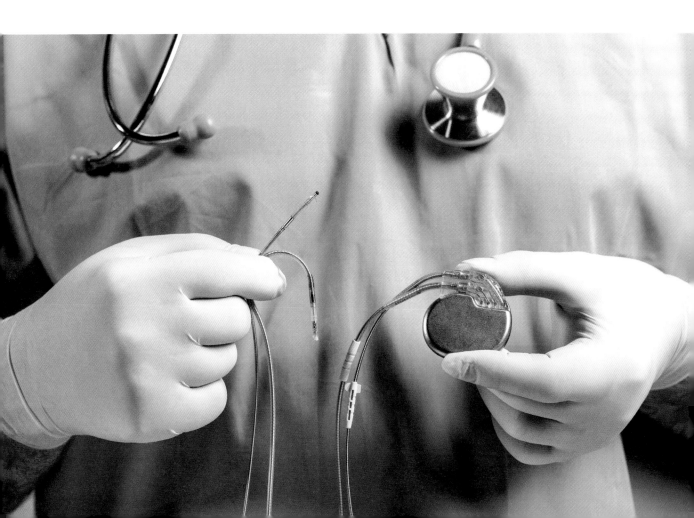

Energy as brain surgery

THE GAMMA KNIFE

More than a million people, many of them suffering from brain tumours, have undergone treatment with the Gamma Knife.

The Gamma Knife is not actually a scalpel – that's what makes it so clever. No incisions, no open wounds, no stitches. Instead, the Gamma Knife works by aiming several high-energy beams (192 to be specific) of gamma radiation at the tumour. The technique was developed by Lars Leksell, a neurosurgeon, together with Börje Larsson, a radiation biologist. Leksell was pursuing his vision of 'bloodless surgery' in the 1940s, when he and Larsson launched a series of experiments that would expand into a brand-new medical discipline known as radiosurgery.

Brain surgery is highly complex. The first successful surgical removals of brain and spinal tumours were performed in London in the late 19th century. In 1922, Herbert Olivecrona carried out the first operation on a brain tumour in Sweden at Seraphim Hospital, a teaching and research hospital affiliated with Stockholm's renowned Karolinska Institutet. Olivecrona pioneered brain surgery in Sweden and became the country's first professor in the subject in 1935.

Lars Leksell was one of Olivecrona's students. He had qualified as a doctor at Karolinska Institutet and went on to secure a position as a surgeon at the Seraphim Hospital. Working as a neurosurgeon under Olivecrona, he refined his talent for finding solutions to the increasingly technical challenges he encountered in his work. After completing his doctoral degree in 1945, Leksell had an opportunity to launch a neurosurgery clinic in Lund. In his pursuit of precision, he developed a steel frame using three-dimensional positioning to calculate the position of the target or tumour. This became known as the *Leksell Stereotactic System*. It enabled surgeons to operate with far greater precision than before. In many cases, operations required only a tiny hole in the skull, just big enough to feed a probe through.

Lars Leksell didn't stop there. He wanted to eliminate all drilling into the skull. After a great deal of experimentation with X-rays, ionizing radiation and ultrasound, he concluded that those forms of radiation were not powerful enough to eliminate tumours. Leksell needed

Nurse Corinne Heldt demonstrates the new Gamma Knife at the Chicago Institute of Neurosurgery and Neuroresearch in 1993. It uses gamma rays to operate on the brain with no need to open the patient's cranium.

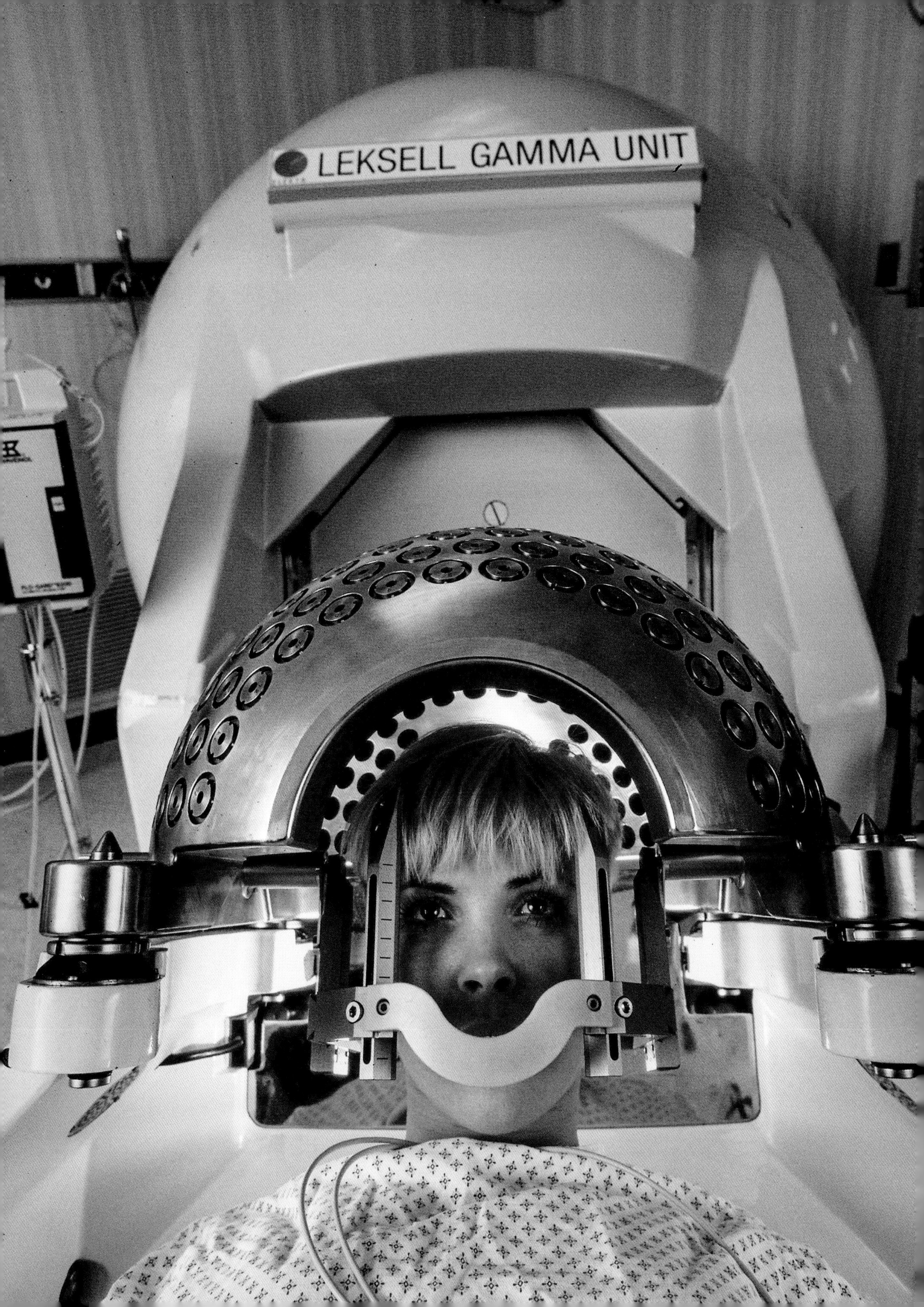
LEKSELL GAMMA UNIT

an expert in radiation. He was appointed professor of neurosurgery at Lund University in 1958 but remained there for just a few years before returning to Karolinska Institutet in Stockholm, where he would spend the rest of his career. That was where he embarked on an important joint project.

Börje Larsson had studied the physical and biological aspects of radiation at the Gustaf Werner Institute of Nuclear Chemistry at Uppsala University. He conducted experiments using proton-beam treatment for tumours. Proton beams are a significantly more powerful form of radiation than the types Leksell had previously worked with. Together, the researchers would aim proton beams at precise locations inside patients' heads, guided by the stereotactic frame. The first operation performed with these focused, high-intensity beams received a great deal of press coverage – the patient's brain tumour was destroyed with no need for an incision in the skull. Yet Herbert Olivecrona, the leading authority in the field, was sceptical. He was unconvinced that radiation would ever replace 'classic neurosurgery'. Leksell was not discouraged. He was certain they were on the right track. When Olivecrona retired in 1960, Leksell took over as head of neurosurgery at the Seraphim Hospital. There was a growing need for a modern radiotherapy facility that was better suited to treating patients. In the early 1960s, a state-of-the-art research institute and clinic began to take shape at Karolinska Institutet.

By that time, Leksell understood that gamma radiation might be a better choice than proton radiation. With their higher energy levels, gamma rays might be more effective at destroying tumours. But switching to gamma rays would entail new challenges. Leksell and Larsson decided to use Cobalt-60 as their radiation source. They conceived of a helmet-like structure that was to be fitted with no fewer than 180 radiation sources, all directed at the precise location for treatment. Constructing it would be no easy task. They received some assistance from an unexpected place. Their chief funding source, the Axel and Margaret Ax:son Johnson Foundation for Public Benefit, has ties to the Axel Johnson Group, a wide-ranging business conglomerate. The group's holdings include Motala Verkstad, one of Sweden's

Over a million brain tumour patients have benefitted from the Gamma Knife since the first operation in 1968. With the latest generation of Gamma Knife technology, surgeons can offer high-precision cranial radiosurgery to more patients with a wider range of tumour sizes and types. The Gamma Knife now integrates advanced positioning and radiation dosing to increase its versatility in radiosurgery.

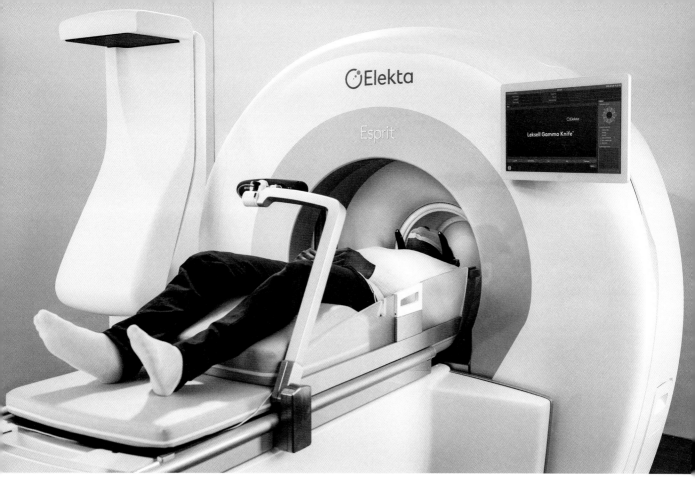

oldest engineering companies. Among the products Motala produced were ships' propellers. The shaft of each propeller contained a precision-drilled channel. The degree of precision used in manufacturing the propeller shafts was comparable to that required for the 180 radiation channels in Leksell's helmet. That's how the Motala engineering firm, 200 years old, ended up producing parts for the world's most advanced radiation surgery equipment.

On 27 January 1968, the first patient underwent surgery with the Leksell Gamma Knife. In 1972, Lars Leksell founded the company Elekta Instrument AB, together with his son Laurent (Larry). The company was later expanded by Lars sons Larry and Dan. For them, the battle against cancer is about taming hazardous beams of radiation and directing them to cure patients – while building a thriving business to support that aim. Every Gamma Knife machine costs several million dollars, but Elekta has managed to disseminate its innovation all over the world. A great many lives have been saved thanks to this technology, with over a million patients treated thus far.

More dazzling smiles

DENTAL IMPLANTS

Titanium screw for a dental implant.

In wealthy countries, statistics show that two thirds of people aged 55 and over have lost at least one tooth. And as we grow older, our teeth get looser. Meanwhile, today's 70-year-olds have very different standards for their appearance compared to previous generations. So the market for dental implants is growing all over the world – notably in developing countries' growing middle classes.

Half a century ago, people who had lost teeth were offered dentures, which were often ugly and uncomfortable. Dental implants were something brand new. As is often the case, medical innovations require both a dedicated figure to spearhead their development, and a smoothly functioning interface between industry, academia and patients.

Per-Ingvar Brånemark qualified as a doctor at Lund University. After completing his PhD on the function of blood circulation in bones and bone marrow, he relocated to Gothenburg in 1960 to learn more about the interaction between bone tissue and blood. He performed experiments on rabbits in the lab. In order to carry out his experiments, he had to construct small hollow implants, called oculars. The oculars were made from titanium. One day, Brånemark made a surprising discovery. When he tried to remove one of the tiny oculars, he was unable to extract it. It seemed to have fused to the rabbit's bone tissue.

Rather than dismiss it as a random occurrence, Brånemark became curious. Normally, the body expels foreign objects. But if a material could be found that reacted with the body's cells and became embedded in tissues instead, it would open up countless new possibilities.

Brånemark's intuition turned out to be right. As it happens, titanium is a metal with very special properties. A brand-new field of research emerged: osseointegration, the science of connecting living bone to other materials. Brånemark began to study the possibilities with teeth.

Just three years later, in 1965, Per-Ingvar Brånemark installed the first titanium dental implants in a patient's mouth. After another three years, he submitted a patent application for a 'permanently implantable anchoring device for a prosthesis or similar'.

Brånemark's dental implants consist of titanium screws that are fixed directly in the jawbone. The bone gradually grows to hold them in place. Then false teeth can be attached to the screws. The teeth are often made of titanium on the inside, with a porcelain crown coloured to match the patient's other teeth.

Proof that the method worked was not enough to convince Brånemark's colleagues, though. Scientists as well as dentists were sceptical. As is often the case with innovations that challenge prevailing views, there was significant resistance. Some people thought the man-made surfaces would provide an ideal environment for bacteria, even providing a 'superhighway' for harmful microorganisms to enter the bloodstream. The conflict reached such proportions that the Swedish National Board of Health and Welfare stepped in and commissioned a study from three independent professors. Their report was unequivocal: Brånemark's dental implants worked.

Next, Brånemark wanted to understand precisely why titanium could fuse with bone tissue. He knew that some scientists at Gothenburg's Chalmers University of Technology were experts at intramolecular behaviour between different materials, so he got in touch with them. At that time, the field of surface physics was developing rapidly, particularly with regard to biomaterials in general and titanium biomaterial surfaces in particular. Brånemark continued to collaborate with Chalmers for more than 20 years. This collaboration has led to a large number of scientific dissertations and a successful cluster of innovative companies. Bioimplantation is now used in many areas besides screws for false teeth. For example, surgeons can now implant hearing aids directly in patients' skulls – helping hundreds of thousands of people with hearing loss all over the world.

Per-Ingvar Brånemark was inspired by the interface between research and industry. Nobelpharma was set up as a subsidiary of Bofors, a Swedish arms manufacturer, in the early 1980s to commercialise production of Brånemark's implants. It was not an initial success, and the division was on the verge of being shut down when it managed to secure a sizeable grant from Sweden's state investment bank. A crucial turning point came in 1982 at a conference in Toronto in Canada, where many delegates had arrived as opponents to dental implants but went home as converts, persuaded by an impressive presentation by

Per-Ingvar Brånemark himself. Nobelpharma soon received a number of orders, and development took off. The company changed its name to Nobel Biocare in 1996. Today it continues to manufacture and sell specialised equipment for dentistry and dental implants.

Per-Ingvar Brånemark always kept patients' needs at the front of his mind. Everyone involved in producing new implants – scientists, product developers, marketers and dentists – were drilled in the importance of focusing on users. That corporate culture lives on today.

But Per-Ingvar Brånemark's legacy extends beyond the manufacture of dental implants. His son Rickard Brånemark has taken osseointegration into new areas. Research into integrating metals and other materials with the skeleton has led to successful new types of prostheses for amputees. These prostheses are developed by Integrum, a company founded by the second-generation Brånemark.

Researchers at Chalmers are now working on prostheses controlled by the mind. This would not have been possible without Per-Ingvar Brånemark's initial discovery and efforts.

After the patient's jawbone has grown around a titanium screw, a replacement tooth can be fastened to the fixed screw by means of a smaller screw. The upper part of the tooth is then glued into place.

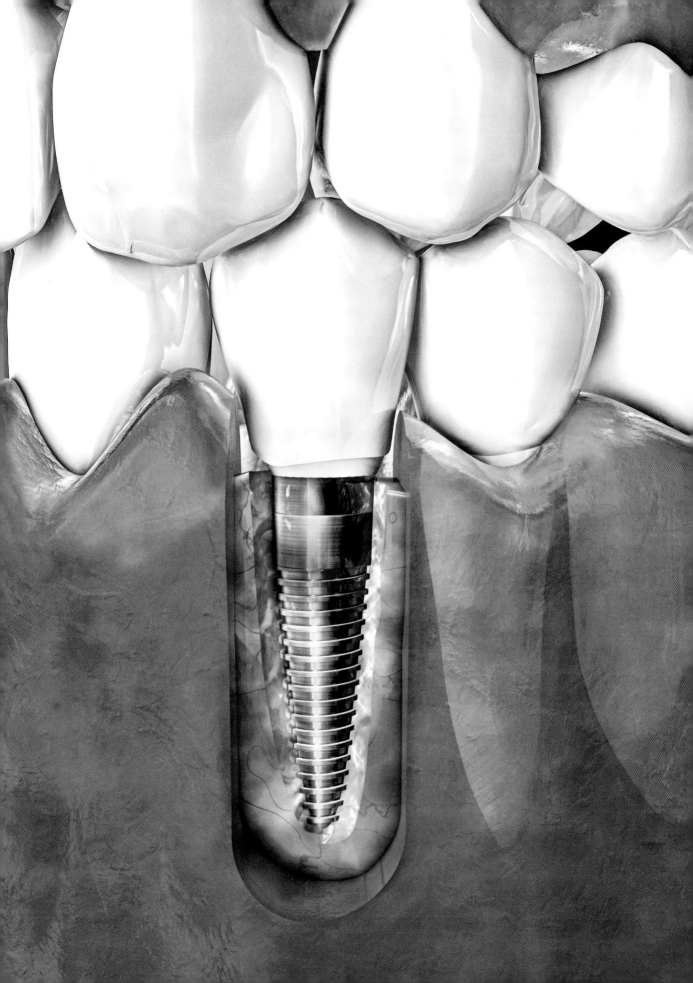

Close to your heart

BABY CARRIER

Mothers from every culture have used shawls and lengths of fabric to create secure baby slings that leave both their hands free. However, this concept had been largely forgotten in the modern Western world until BabyBjörn produced its simple, practical baby carrier in 1973. In the decades since then, the company has grown and refined its baby carriers, which are now used all over the globe.

It was no accident that the baby carrier was born in Sweden at a time when views of equal parenting were taking shape in Swedish society.

Sweden's economy boomed after the Second World War. Policies to create a strong welfare state, based on the idea of the country as the 'people's home' (*folkhemmet* in Swedish), gained strong support. They influenced people's views on lifestyles and home furnishings, raising children and division of labour in the home. Inequality came under increasing criticism in the 1960s, and women's liberation was part of the modernisation effort. In that spirit, the role of the housewife was phased out in favour of a modern family, where men were encouraged to play a larger part in their children's lives and around the home. This shift was accelerated by new tax legislation that abolished joint taxation of married couples, thereby reducing incentives for married women to stay at home.

BabyBjörn, a company founded in 1961 by Björn Jakobson and his sister-in-law Elsa Jakobson, sold a variety of useful products to make life easier for parents of babies and small children. Their first big seller was the 'babysitter', a fabric-covered bouncer seat Björn Jakobson had developed after a trip to the United States. That was followed by a plastic bib with a moulded pocket to catch food, and an inflatable changing mat and various potties and bathroom stools.

In 1962, Björn Jakobson met a young designer at a dance. The two of them clicked, and Björn and Lillemor were married a few months later. The couple proved to have a winning combination of skills. After studying social sciences, Björn had travelled widely. With his strong entrepreneurial streak, he picked up many new ideas on his travels. Lillemor was more artistic, with degrees in both advertising and textile design. Soon they had both a family and a business together.

BabyBjörn understood what modern families need. Both parents can be close to their child, with their hands free.

The baby carrier was their first big success. It was developed as a practical response to an academic query. At that time, Björn Jakobson was in touch with a number of paediatricians, including John Lind of Karolinska Children's Hospital (now Astrid Lindgren Children's Hospital). Lind, a forward-thinking doctor, alerted Jakobson to new research into the importance of physical contact in children's development. The idea that touch was crucial – particularly for the development of babies' brains – was revolutionary. And it applied to more than just contact between mother and child. John Lind is known for saying: 'With the birth of the child comes the birth of the family.'

That gave Björn Jakobson some food for thought. Not long after that meeting, BabyBjörn launched its first baby carrier. 'I felt like I was floating on a cloud,' Björn Jakobson said, describing the first time he carried his daughter Josefin close to his heart. The carrier was named *Hjärtenära*, meaning 'close to the heart'.

Much of the baby carrier's success was due to its superior ergonomics, but the design and fabrics also played an important part. For example, a nautical-inspired model released in 1991 was a huge decade-long success on the export market. A few years later, a navy blue BabyBjörn carrier was pictured in an upscale American fashion magazine. The black-and-white photo made readers think the carrier was black. Word reached Lillemor Jakobson, who immediately sensed an opportunity. She produced a model in black fabric featuring a discreet logo. Prior to that, most baby accessories used to come in pastel colours, often decorated with cute animals. BabyBjörn's 'Black Gingham' model took the market by storm. Suddenly royalty, business executives and sports stars were seen wearing the baby carrier.

A new name joined the ranks of world-famous Swedish Björns alongside tennis star Björn Borg and Björn Ulvaeus from ABBA. In the early 21st century there was talk of the 'babybjornification of American dads'. It's likely that this innovation created by Lillemor and Björn Jakobson has led to more and more children's closeness to their parents – particularly their fathers.

Governed equality

PARENTAL LEAVE FOR BOTH PARENTS

Throughout history, women have looked after babies and small children while also doing jobs to enable their families to survive. With industrialisation came a differentiation between people's home and work, and the role of the housewife arose. It was taken for granted that a woman would leave her job when she became a mother.

After the First World War, working women campaigned for paid leave to look after their infant children. The right to maternity leave was also part of the platform formulated by the International Labour Organization (ILO), established in 1919 as part of the Treaty of Versailles. Many countries introduced legislation that entitled women to unpaid leave, which was not much help to poor working-class families.

After the Second World War, paid maternity leave of some sort for new mothers became common in many industrialised countries. In Sweden, maternity benefit was replaced by maternity insurance in the 1950s, which entitled new mothers to 90 days' paid leave.

Maternity benefit was both radical and conservative. It enabled women with children to remain in the labour market. But at the same time, it cemented the man's role as the main breadwinner and the woman's responsibility for children and the home.

In Sweden, this model started to come into question in the 1970s. The notion that women and men had equal responsibilities in a marriage had gained ground for a number of reasons. Partly it was a matter of economics: there was a labour shortage, and 300,000 housewives would be a welcome addition to the workforce. But criticism of the traditional patriarchal family had also increased since the 1960s. The growing feminist movement demanded equality between men and women both in the workplace and at home. The birth control pill had ushered in a new sexual freedom, while the introduction of individual taxation for married couples in 1969 eliminated their previous advantage of joint taxation.

In the spring of 1974, the Swedish parliament passed a historic law. Sweden became the first country in the world to introduce paid parental leave for both men and women. All the political parties agreed on the bill, but the liberal People's Party (Folkpartiet) disagreed with the

In 1974, Sweden was the first country in the world to introduce paid parental leave for both parents. Today, Swedish fathers take a third of the nation's total parental leave.

provision that stated parents could decide who would use the leave. They were worried that the new parental leave would become a trap for women, tying them down to housework and childcare. They wanted a system in which paid leave was divided equally between parents.

Their concern was justified, as it turned out. In 1995 – two decades after the introduction of shared parental leave – fathers accounted for just 9 per cent of all parental leave. In order to accelerate the pace of change, a 'fatherhood month' was introduced. If a father did not take that month of leave, it was lost. In the early 2000s, the quota was increased to two months. It seemed to have an effect. The share of parental leave taken by men has increased steadily since then, from 16 per cent in 2005 to 19 per cent in 2011 and 30 per cent in 2020.

Whether the glass is half full or half empty is in the eye of the beholder. But if you look at things in the longer term, shared parental leave is still a historic transformation.

Connecting to the future

AXE TELEPHONE EXCHANGE

Using the telephone seems straightforward – you dial a number, and someone answers. But what happens in between? In the earliest systems, a signal travelled along a wire between two telephones. But if the new devices were going to be of any practical use, they had to be part of a network that would allow users to phone whoever they wanted. It required an exchange, where an incoming call could be connected to any other line in the system.

The first solution was to employ switchboard operators to manually insert telephone plugs into a panel containing an array of jacks. Telephone companies liked to give an impression of their capacity by using images in their advertisements showing long rows of smartly dressed female telephone operators in grand surroundings. A skilled operator could handle around 250 calls an hour – an impressive number, but not enough to meet demand. It was also an expensive option as the telephone network expanded ever further.

The automatic telephone exchange was a more efficient solution. It was invented in the early 20th century and refined further after the First World War. When a caller dialled a number on their Bakelite telephone, each digit sent an electric pulse to the exchange, where relays were switched in complex sequences so that the signal could reach the telephone the caller had dialled.

This sort of electromechanical exchange was the dominant type for decades. In the 1960s, though, major telephone companies began developing different types of electronic exchanges. Ericsson – already a successful Swedish engineering firm under its former name of LM Ericsson – came out with an early exchange which bore the product name AKE. But it had many drawbacks and could not outcompete the traditional exchanges.

In the late 1960s, LM Ericsson decided to develop a new exchange based on its experiences with the AKE exchange. Even so, there was some resistance within the company against the new digital technology. To bolster its competence in this field, LM Ericsson launched a joint venture with Televerket, the Swedish state telephone authority, which was also experiencing dissent among its engineers. To overcome these issues, LM Ericsson and Televerket created an R&D joint

A telephone exchange in London during the Second World War. All calls were connected manually by plugging in wires.

venture called Ellemtel with 500 employees. The idea was to foster a creative environment outside the two organisations' traditional corporate cultures.

Opponents of the new technology argued that electromechanical exchanges were still selling well. If their side had prevailed, Ericsson might have vanished from the market in the 1970s. That's what happened to Facit, another highly successful Swedish manufacturing corporation, after it chose not to invest in digital technology. In just a few years, Facit went from being a global market leader to virtual bankruptcy, outcompeted by new electronic calculators and word processors.

AXE, the product name of the new exchange, cost 500 million Swedish kronor to develop – an enormous sum at that time. Rapid computerisation made the technology feasible, but the crucial factor in the success of the new exchange was its unique flexibility. The AXE system was based on an advanced modular concept, with modules that were easy to swap out and combine in different ways.

The first orders, for relatively modest systems, came in from France. By the end of the 1970s it was clear that the AXE exchange would be a huge success. LM Ericsson secured major orders over its competitors ITT and Western Electric to supply Australia and Saudi Arabia. By the early 1990s, the exchange had been sold to 101 countries. Through the years it has been one of Ericsson's top-selling lines.

The development of the AXE telephone exchange is an example of the results that can be achieved through cooperation between public and private organisations. Perhaps it also shows the importance of working on new ideas even when the old ways are still working well.

The first AXE exchange was installed in 1976. It consisted of a large number of modules that were easy to replace, enabling new functions to be added.

Moving forward

THE ROLLATOR

Aina Wifalk suffered from polio when she was 21 years old. The disease affected her badly, but eventually it led to one of the most important innovations for people whose bodies need support in their daily lives – the rollator.

In 1949, Aina Wifalk had just started studying to become a nurse. She started to feel ill, with a sore throat and fatigue, but those symptoms soon gave way to muscle cramps that radiated down to her feet. She was admitted to hospital. Within a month of her initial mild symptoms, she was unable to stand or walk.

The illness forced Wifalk to drop out of her nursing course. But it did not prevent her from studying, and eventually she got a job as a hospital counsellor. She had a real talent for helping people with various disabilities. She got around with the help of two long walking sticks.

Aina Wifalk was a driving force in welfare issues and established a number of patients' associations, including groups for people with multiple sclerosis and victims of traffic accidents. By the mid-1970s, though, her shoulders had suffered damage, and her life became more restricted. At night she would lie awake and wonder how she could regain at least some mobility.

Perhaps she was inspired by the book trolleys used by librarians; perhaps she thought of kicksleds with metal runners that were commonly used in winter at that time. When she had formulated her idea – a walking frame on wheels – she submitted a proposal to a government innovation fund, which gave her a small grant and put her in contact with a fabricator. Besides four wheels, Wifalk wanted her device to have handles and brakes, and it should also be collapsible for easy transport. She knew which features were important. That was in 1978, and production began three years later.

Looking back, we can say that Aina Wifalk's innovation has become a means to give people their freedom back. She never patented the rollator, since she wanted the innovation to spread freely. Before she passed away at the age of 55 in 1983, she was delighted to see that her rollator was gaining users in many countries. In Sweden it is used by every third person over the age of 80.

Aina Wifalk was affected by polio and had difficulty walking. She solved the problem by designing a wheeled walking frame that was further refined into the modern-day rollator.

At the touch of a button

MOBILE PHONE 'CALL' BUTTON

Not many people are familiar with Laila Ohlgren. But billions of people use her innovation every day when they press the green button on their mobile phone to make a call.

For most people – particularly younger folks – it's natural to dial a phone number first and then press the 'call' button. But that's not how things worked with old-fashioned landline phones. In those days, you had to pick up the receiver (shaped like the symbol on the green button) to get a line and then use the buttons or rotary dial to input a sequence of digits to call another telephone.

Those steps were also used on the first mobile telephones on the market in the 1980s. But early mobile networks had patchy coverage and often suffered outages, especially if you were on the move. There was a high risk of losing a connection or losing numbers when dialling.

This is where Laila Ohlgren, the first female engineer at the Swedish state telephone authority, comes in. She joined the authority in 1956 at the age of 19 and obtained an engineering degree later on. In the late 1970s she was working on NMT, the Nordic mobile telephony project. It was one of the world's first wireless telephone networks.

Shortly before the launch of NMT in 1981, she hit upon a solution to the dialling problem with mobile phones. Instead of transmitting the digits one by one, you could incorporate a button that would send the entire telephone number that had been dialled all at once. That eliminated the danger that the signal for any digit would be lost in a mobile black spot.

In 2009, Laila Ohlgren was awarded the Polhem Prize, Sweden's most prestigious award for engineering. She died in 2014 at the age of 76. By that time, her green button had been a standard feature on mobile phones all over the world for 30 years.

The green button is one of the simplest and yet most significant innovations for mobile phones.

One step ahead

MOBILE BROADBAND

There's a maxim that every new form of communication is a blend of two earlier forms. One example of this is mobile telephones, which came about when radio met landlines. Then the real revolution came when mobile phones met the internet. Without the Swedish zeal for standardisation and Ericsson's capacity for innovation, though, the telecom industry's 'mobile miracle' wouldn't have worked.

In the early years of mobile telephony, the world was a patchwork of national and regional systems. These divisions were an obstacle to the development of new and internationally, compatible systems. One clear example of the barriers that existed was the ban on transporting radio transmitters across national borders. So, in addition to numerous technical incompatibilities, it was actually illegal to take a mobile phone to another country.

The European Commission called for a European standard that would allow consumers to use their mobile phones everywhere in the internal market. That prompted something of a war between competing technologies, with various countries and companies pressing for the adoption of their own specification as the continental standard. Ericsson's proposal was deemed to be superior, and not just because of its greater range. The Swedish company's concept aimed for full mobile coverage, including in remote forests. One side benefit for the more densely populated areas of Europe was that Ericsson's technology required fewer cellular base stations, making it easier to implement.

Following the selection of a technical specification based on Ericsson's proposal, a standard was launched in 1992 across Europe under the name GSM, which stands for Global System for Mobile communications. That marked the mobile system's move from radio technology to digital.

GSM, also known as 2G, expanded even faster than expected. Market forces made it an increasingly dominant standard. That was a major triumph for Ericsson. For the company's engineers, though, it was clear that within just a few years, the network would be so saturated that sales of mobile base stations would dry up. They started to experiment with increased bandwidth as a possible way to expand the

When Ericsson started experimenting with increased bandwidth for mobile telephony in the 1990s, it had no idea what it would later be used for. It would still be many years before people started using mobile phones for purposes other than making phone calls.

market. The internet was not in widespread use yet, and the people at Ericsson could only speculate about possible uses for mobile broadband. They thought the internet ought to be available wherever people could talk on their mobile phones.

The new digital technology made it possible for designers to shrink mobile phones to pocket size. Mobile ownership started to explode around the turn of the millennium, aided by falling acquisition and running costs. Mobiles were increasingly seen as communication tools for more than just voice calls, as people started sending text messages (also known as SMS, which stands for 'short message service') and soon accessing the internet and email.

The expansion of mobile data traffic required the adoption of standardised technology to ensure international operability. Another battle for supremacy broke out among telecoms giants, this time for mobile broadband standards.

Ericsson had an advantage after having worked on this issue for years and emerged victorious once more. Its solution, originally called WCDMA (not exactly a name that tripped off the tongue), later came to be known as 3G. The international telecom consortia decided that if the new standard was to be implemented globally, all patents required to fulfil the standard had to be available to all members in exchange for a limited fee.

While 3G technology was still under development before the turn of the millennium, it started to become clear that the internet would come to dominate mobile communications. Ericsson came up with some additional features that would enable the new 3G network to handle expanded data traffic. Some outside observers thought the extra investment was wasted. One American analyst declared that nobody will ever want to watch videos on a phone.

As mobile broadband data traffic exploded, around a decade after Ericsson had started developing the technology, the bandwidth was already in place. New iPhone and Android models were taking the world by storm, and they needed mobile broadband. By 2009, two years after the launch of the original iPhone, the global network carried more data than voice traffic.

Today, seven billion users around the world can count on global compatibility for mobile phones and mobile data traffic, which is the result of Swedish innovation, international agreements and global standards.

Following on from 4G, mobile networks are now being upgraded to 5G, still based on Ericsson's standards. Data traffic is expected to grow by several thousand per cent, and bandwidth will be needed for video calls, video and music streaming as well as robots, self-driving vehicles and many more gadgets for the smart home – functionalities that require lightning-fast data transfer across the mobile network.

As base stations have shrunk in size, their capacity has increased almost beyond comprehension. The new 5G network is expected to handle up to a million devices per square kilometre.

Easy to stomach

OMEPRAZOLE (LOSEC)

A healthy person has a thousand wishes; a sick person, only one. That ancient proverb still holds true today. But now stomach ulcer sufferers can be cured quickly, thanks to an innovation that has become one of Sweden's biggest export successes of all time – a medicine called omeprazole, also known by the brand name Losec.

'Translational research' is a new name for a tried-and-trusted technique. Scientists start from the patient's condition to figure out what could have caused it. When they have found the problem, they try to find a solution, which can lead to improved diagnostics and therapies. The result might be a brand-new medicine.

That's how it happened with omeprazole, a medicine used for ulcers and other gastrointestinal disorders. It was launched in the late 1980s, but the story stretches back to the early 1950s and a group of young doctors and pharmacists who were willing to think outside the box. In those days, pharmacies often manufactured medicines themselves, based more on tradition than scientific evidence. Meanwhile, pharmaceutical companies' R&D departments often brought out new preparations without subjecting them to thorough clinical testing on patients. Today, all new medicines must undergo testing to identify any side effects and to prove their scientifically documented effects. This results not only in safer medications, but also longer lead times and higher costs. Ten to 20 years is not an unusual timescale between a discovery in the lab and a new packet of tablets in the pharmacy.

Omeprazole's long journey began in Hässleholm and continued later in Gothenburg, at Hässle, a pharmaceutical company that was part of the Astra corporation. A new research team, led by the bold Head of Research Ivan Östholm, gathered competent scientists from both the university and the hospital. Professors Björn Folkow (physiology), Arvid Carlsson (pharmacology), Leif Hallberg (medicine), Lars Werkö (medicine and cardiology) and surgeon Lars Olbe from Sahlgrenska University Hopsital, with a special interest in ulcers, all played a crucial part.

This innovative collaborative model, with a clear translational element, proved to be extremely fruitful. Omeprazole is just one of many successful results.

One of the first studies the group undertook examined how various medications are absorbed by the intestines. That was followed by studies of iron absorption and causes of iron deficiency. In the 1960s, a large number of scientists were recruited from academia by the pharmaceutical industry. They were given a great deal of freedom to determine their own research. This is a crucial piece of the puzzle for understanding their success. By allowing scientists to retain their academic roles while also working for Hässle, their work naturally benefitted from cross-fertilisation across basic research, applied projects and clinical studies.

Researchers in the Hässle network met twice a year to discuss their challenges and opportunities. These conferences played an important role in the company's development and as a way of identifying new projects. A conference held in 1966 concluded with a keynote speech by Lars Olbe. His message was simple: peptic ulcers were a disorder crying out for treatment with new, modern pharmaceuticals. Wasn't that something worth investing in?

There was a huge need. Estimates showed that around 10 per cent of the population in Western countries would develop an ulcer during their life, and many people were chronic sufferers. Peptic ulcers are caused when the lining of the stomach or the first part of the small intestine is damaged. Scientists knew there was a connection with the production of hydrochloric acid in the stomach. They also knew that reducing stomach acid production could reduce the formation of ulcers. Medicines were available that could neutralise stomach acid, but their effects were short-lived. The most effective treatment available was surgical removal of the affected area, or removal of the nerves that stimulated acid production.

Hässle recruited Lars Olbe to join its team. As an expert in regulating stomach acid production, he established a gastric research laboratory dubbed 'Gastlab'. The lab soon became a creative interdisciplinary hub. Researchers improved their knowledge of what a gastric ulcer actually is. Before long, they were able to transfer their new chemical and clinical knowledge to the laboratory and conduct tests. Soon they had a brand-new preparation to present. It was given the generic name *omeprazole*.

Omeprazole was a new type of medication known as a proton pump inhibitor. This complex molecule was activated precisely where it was needed: in the specialised cells in the stomach wall that produce hydrochloric acid. It blocked the proton pump mechanism in the cell membrane, so the acid could not be released. No one had ever managed to achieve this result with a medicine before. The block was so targeted and effective that acid production in the stomach essentially stopped.

But the development process was long, and there were several occasions when Astra's executives wanted to shut down Gastlab. Lars Olbe rallied his colleagues and argued in favour of the investment.

After 22 years of hard work and countless studies, omeprazole was launched in 1988 under the brand name Losec. The medication was effective, but patients' ulcers often returned when they stopped taking the medicine. The root cause of peptic ulcers remained a mystery. Stress and poor diet had long been suspected. In the early 1980s, two Australian scientists, Barry Marshall and Robin Warren, made the revolutionary discovery that peptic ulcers are caused by a bacterial infection. Their research earned them the 2005 Nobel Prize in medicine.

Thanks to that research, we now know that the bacterium *Helicobacter pylori* lives and reproduces in the stomach lining of half the world's population. In poor countries, virtually everyone is infected. In countries like Sweden, the figure is around one in three. Fortunately, not everyone who has the bacteria will get sick. But around 10–15 per cent will get gastritis or stomach ulcers.

Antibiotics are used to fight bacteria. But omeprazole also had an important part to play here. A course of treatment combining a proton-

pump inhibitor with at least two types of antibiotics cured 90 per cent of patients. And they remained healthy in the longer term. The bacteria were killed, and the ulcers did not return.

As more ulcers are treated, the rate of stomach cancer – the fifth most common type of cancer around the world – is also decreasing. There is a link between chronic inflammation and tumour growth. For a time, omeprazole was the world's best-selling medicine ever. In the mid-1990s, sales accounted for nearly half of Astra's turnover.

Another Nobel Prize-awarded team helped to achieve further developments of omeprazole. In 2001, Barry Sharpless, William Knowles and Ryoji Noyori shared the prize for chemistry for a method of asymmetric synthesis, enabling production of just one version of a molecule that is normally formed in two symmetrical versions. Omeprazole occurs in one effective version and another mirror-image version of its molecule. Astra Zeneca's scientists used asymmetric synthesis to develop esomeprazole (also known as Nexium), which only contains the form of the molecule that works best in the body. With fewer side effects, it also became a best-seller.

Pharmaceutical companies need to keep coming up with innovative new products. Patents on medicines only remain valid for a certain number of years, after which other companies can manufacture and sell the same active substance under their own name. These are called generic medicines. They help to reduce medicine costs for consumers, so that more people can afford to stay healthy.

In the air and at sea

THE STDMA NAVIGATION SYSTEM

Around 8,000 planes are in the air at any given time. Every second of every day. Håkan Lans is the Swedish inventor behind STDMA, the navigation system that helps aircraft steer clear of one another. The system has also become standard for ships at sea.

Lans grew up in Stockholm in the 1950s. Post-war optimism was underpinned by faith in new technology. Technology could seemingly solve any problem. That mindset appealed to young Håkan. His mother encouraged him to be curious. When her son's questions became too difficult for her to answer, she would visit the local library and borrow books. She marked the pages where Håkan could find the answers he was looking for.

For Håkan Lans, there wasn't much of a dividing line between things that would be amazing if they existed, and things that were actually possible to achieve. At the age of 12, he built a soapbox car with an engine. A few years later, the family's kitchen blew up – the result of Håkan's failed attempt to launch a rocket.

But he was not discouraged. Quite the reverse – he found it incredibly rewarding to turn his ideas into reality. Inspired by Jacques Cousteau's book *The Silent World*, at the age of 18 he started working on the world's smallest submarine. Lans managed to persuade one company to give him some storage batteries and another to construct the engines he had designed. He could now travel 90 metres below the water's surface in his own mini-submarine.

That feat attracted a great deal of attention, and Lans became something of a celebrity. But when his call-up papers for mandatory military service landed in his letterbox, he was worried. How was he going to work on his sub and do his service at the same time? Lans decided to pick up the phone and ring Sweden's defence minister, and soon Lans had a tailor-made role as a research assistant at Sweden's National Defence Research Institute. The post also had ties to Stockholm University. To his delight, Lans now had access to workshops, advanced equipment and clever colleagues. He came up with one bold project proposal after another. In the years that followed, he created a large number of inventions, including a special camera for underwater use,

Following pages: Around 90 per cent of traded goods are transported by sea. Since the Swedish STDMA system became mandatory and ships can be tracked, not only has the risk of a collision been reduced but also there has been a decrease in the handling of illegal goods.

colour computer graphics and an early version of a computer mouse. But the creation that would make the biggest impact on the world stage was his navigation system.

The idea came to him when he was sailing. He had read about the American satellite navigation system that would later be called Global Positioning System (GPS). Lans reasoned that it was nice to know your own location, but a system that could prevent collisions would have to combine each user's location with the locations of other users on the same map. All positions had to be specified with their latitude, longitude and altitude, plus a time stamp. And how would all the aircraft and ground locations communicate with each other? Creating a radio link to do all that would be difficult. Lans realised that in order to achieve fast and efficient data transfer, the data link had to be fully automated and self-organised – so he needed to construct a system more complex than any human could control or monitor. It took 10 years just to program the simulator.

Despite setbacks and challenges, on 1 July 1991 Håkan Lans obtained a patent on his system. The name STDMA stands for 'Self-organizing Time-Division Multiple Access'. The system combines GPS signals with radio communications for the automatic tracking of multiple users. The fact that the Swedish system has become mandatory in shipping means that all ships now have an eye on each other. This has meant a huge step forward for security at sea.

When the system was being considered as a candidate for a new mandatory world standard for aviation, it had to undergo an independent simulation and evaluation. The European Commission paid 200 million euros for those tests. In 2014, STDMA was selected as the global standard for air traffic. In addition to increasing air safety, it helps airlines to optimise flight routes, thereby shortening flight times and avoiding delays.

For reasons of industrial policy, it is not yet mandatory. However, a letter signed by the president of the European Patent Office and other top officials noted that it is extremely rare for a project to make it this far. The letter concludes with a recognition of Håkan Lans: 'But as shown by its success, his self-belief took him right to the top.'

Keep rocking

TWO IMPORTANT BLOOD SAMPLE TOOLS

Some people go to work, do their job and go home. Then there are those who identify a problem and don't give up until they have solved it. Barbro Hjalmarsson was the second type of person. She was a nurse who was tired of manipulating test tubes.

Nurses' daily duties in the mid-20th century included performing a large number of time-consuming blood tests. Test tubes containing blood samples had to be inverted or tilted at regular intervals, otherwise the blood would clot, making it impossible to conduct the necessary tests. Each test tube had to be tilted 10–15 times – all while the nurse was supposed to be taking new blood samples.

Barbro Hjalmarsson invented a device that rocked test tubes back and forth, freeing her up to deal with the next patient. At the age of 75, she applied for a patent on her 'test-tube cradle' in 1994. She worked with Triolab, a medical equipment manufacturer, to mass-produce the device, which was sold under the name TriomiX. She later sold the patent to Triolab, which still markets several different models. The device has a plastic tray that can rock six to ten test tubes back and forth. TriomiX runs on rechargeable batteries. Its simplicity and usefulness ensure that thousands of TriomiX are still in use in healthcare.

But this is not Barbro Hjalmarsson's only innovation. She also pioneered a method to measure erythrocyte sedimentation rate, a statistic that gives an indication of inflammation in a patient's body. When an inflammatory condition is present, the person's erythrocytes (red blood cells) tend to clump together. This clumping is influenced by the combination of proteins in blood plasma, which is affected by inflammation or infection.

Barbro Hjalmarsson realised that clotted blood cells in blood samples were denser than individual cells, which caused the clots to settle at the bottom of a test tube. She added a substance that separated the blood cells from the plasma in a sample. After an hour, she measured how many millimetres of pale blood plasma remained at the top of the tall, thin tube. That reading was established as the sedimentation rate. It can vary between a few millimetres and over 10 centimetres. The faster the blood cells settle, the higher the sedimentation rate. Today, Hjalmarsson's method is used all over the world.

Test-tube cradles are found in clinics and hospitals all over Scandinavia. Nurses no longer need to invert test tubes manually.

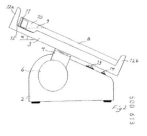

154

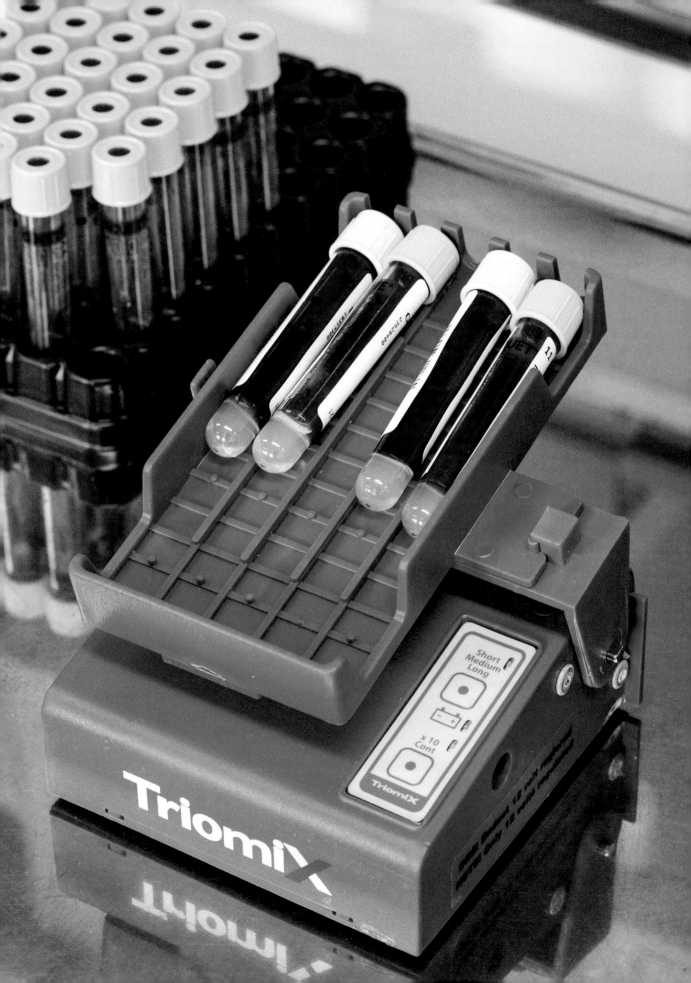

Use your head

INCREASING HELMET SAFETY WITH MIPS

The human brain weighs just over a kilogram (2.2 lb). Yet it generates our thoughts and feelings, stores our memories – and regulates everything that happens in our bodies. It is the most complex structure we know of. The brain consists of over 100 billion nerve cells, each of which can send signals to thousands of other cells at a speed of 300 km/h. The brain is also by far our most delicate organ. As we zoom along on our bike or down a ski slope, we want to be as well protected as we can be. Having a Mips system integrated in your helmet can significantly increase safety. This innovation has been integrated in more than 150 helmet brands all over the world.

In 1995, the brain surgeon Hans von Holst at Stockholm's Karolinska Institutet got in touch with KTH Royal Institute of Technology in Stockholm to initiate a research project into injury prevention. Von Holst aimed to combine clinical and technical expertise to reduce damage to accident victims' central nervous systems. He founded the Department of Neuronics to undertake interdisciplinary biomechanical research to prevent head and neck injuries.

That same year, Peter Halldin began his PhD on cranial and neck injury prevention, and research was underway. After just a year, von Holst and Halldin were ready to present the basic concept that would become Mips – the Multi-directional Impact Protection System. Inspiration came from the anatomy of the head. The brain is shielded from rotational forces because the cerebrospinal fluid helps it to slide against the inside of the skull. Von Holst and Halldin also confirmed that many cases of brain damage were caused by oblique impacts to the head, resulting in rotation.

Svein Kleiven, another PhD student, was brought on board at KTH to produce what would become one of the world's most advanced models of the human brain. The model was a crucial tool for measuring the effects of different Mips prototypes on the brain's inner structure. Mips consists of a low-friction layer mounted inside the helmet. In a crash, the low-friction layer is designed to move slightly along with the head to redirect harmful rotational forces away from the head.

The first helmet equipped with a Mips system was tested in 2000. It

A helmet with Mips has a layer-on-layer system in which the different layers absorb movements from different directions.

A cycle helmet is tested in Mips' test lab. The helmet is mounted on a plastic head and dropped from a height of two metres. Researchers use sensors to observe how the different layers absorb rotational forces.

resulted in a paper published in a scientific journal the following year. Now Hans von Holst and his team could point to scientific evidence for their innovation. In 2001, Peter Halldin, Hans von Holst and Svein Kleiven founded Mips AB. They produced their own riding helmet with Mips technology, but soon, with the help of venture capital firm HealthCap, pivoted to a different strategy that would prove to be crucial in the spread of the technology. Mips would focus on becoming the leading creator of the technology, continuously improving and adapting solutions for different helmet types. The company's customers were not individual consumers, but rather helmet manufacturers around the world. The manufacturers could make their own products safer – and thus more competitive – by integrating Mips safety systems into their helmets.

An important milestone was reached in 2015, with over a million Mips units sold. Two years later – on 23 March 2017, to be precise – Mips AB was floated on the Stockholm stock exchange. Today, Mips units are present in more than 30 million helmets for alpine skiing, cycling, equestrian sports, climbing and motorcycle riding.

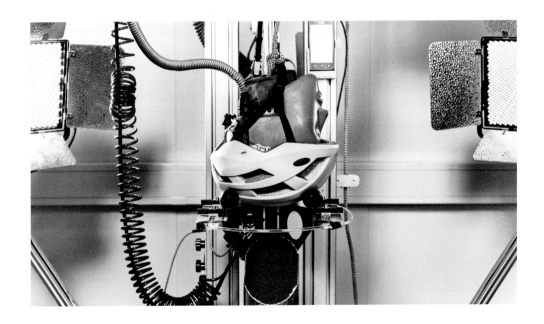

Close connectivity

BLUETOOTH

This is the story of how an ancient Viking king lent his name to a communications technology that's part of more than five billion devices all over the world. Anyone who has ever connected a wireless mouse to a computer or talked on the phone through their vehicle's built-in speakers and microphone has used this technology.

It all started at the Department of Applied Electronics at Lund University, where Sven Mattisson arrived after qualifying as a civil engineer in 1979. Lennart Stigmark, a legendary professor, had just retired from the department, but his preference for working with radio waves still held sway. While many were captivated by the possibilities of digital technologies, Stigmark had urged his younger colleagues, 'Whatever you do, don't forget about analogue technology!' Without Stigmark's appreciation of radio waves, which emanate from a continuous analogue signal rather than digital zeroes and ones, this story would have come to a swift end.

Engineering expertise with radio waves was vital when the Swedish telecoms giant Ericsson relocated its mobile phone development business to Lund. Ericsson and the university's Department of Applied Electronics continued to develop closer ties in the early 1980s. Following a stint as an exchange student at the California Institute of Technology, Sven Mattisson worked on a large number of different components. He developed a circuit simulator that simulated analogue behaviour in an integrated circuit. After completing his PhD at Lund, Mattisson began working for Ericsson Mobile Communications in 1995.

There he joined Nils Rydbeck, another expert in radio engineering, who had been puzzling over whether cables connecting headsets and other accessories could be replaced with a radio link. What if you could eliminate the cables? Mattisson was given a tough assignment. Working with Jaap Haartsen, an engineer from the Netherlands, he was to investigate the feasibility of creating a short-range, low-power wireless radio connection between devices such as a computer and a telephone. It was also a challenge to fit all the necessary components into a tiny space, as in a mobile phone. They also had to reduce power consumption to a minimum, while also generating sufficient range.

$$H\ (\ast) + B\ (\text{B}) = \text{Bluetooth symbol}$$

And it couldn't cost more than US$5! Mattisson and Haartsen came up with a brilliant solution, which they called the Multi-Communicator Link, or MC-link for short. Sven Mattisson found a practical use for the technology he had worked on during his time in California. By compromising between system and hardware design, the engineers could build a radio as a single circuit with inexpensive standard components. One key feature was its ability to rapidly swap between radio frequencies (channels) to reduce the effects of various types of interference. If one signal was too weak, a different frequency band could be used. Thus, they could use weak signals and the link would still work, even in high-noise environments.

In 1997 a consortium was launched with Intel. It wasn't long before other big players – IBM, Nokia and Toshiba – joined in. These competitors realised that a standardised solution was the best way forward for everyone. If they all incorporated the same technology in their devices, all the phones, computers, speakers and microphones would be able to recognise each other and communicate when they came within range, no matter what brand name was printed on the outside. Paradoxically, this rapid advance in technology could bring competitors together on a workable long-term solution.

The name 'Bluetooth' originated in a bar in Toronto, where Sven Mattisson and Jim Kardach, an engineer with Intel, were chatting after pitching their proposals for new radio systems. Kardach was fascinated by the Vikings, and Mattisson told him about a classic adventure novel by Frans G. Bengtsson entitled *The Long Ships*, which tells the story of how the Danish king Harald 'Bluetooth' Gormsson united Viking clans from different parts of Scandinavia. After a couple of beers, the similarity with MC-Link's ability to facilitate wireless communication seemed obvious and the term Bluetooth was invented.

Bluetooth technology has played a key role in enabling more and more devices to be connected to the 'internet of things'. We can now install wireless cameras and alarm systems in our homes, as well as smart thermostats and cleaning devices. We can control the lights, use voice-controlled smart speakers and rely on smart baby monitors. But this is only the beginning. Bluetooth is here to stay.

Calling for free

SKYPE

Ten years after the launch of this innovation, the *Oxford English Dictionary* added a new verb: *skype*. By that time, you could also see the other person while you were talking – or rather, *skyping*.

Sweden has a long history of computer programming and software development. In 1953, BESK was up and running at KTH Royal Institute of Technology in Stockholm. It was the world's fastest calculating machine – the word 'computer' was not in use yet. Saab became the first company to use this new calculating machine in the aeronautics industry and led its development in the 1960s and 1970s. BESK took up an entire room, but rapid progress made computers more compact and brought them ever closer to people over the following decades.

Swedish schools were quick to catch on, and Katedralskolan in Uppsala has long been at the leading edge. In the 1980s, computers were available for pupils to use. Teachers often found themselves learning from their pupils rather than the other way round.

One of the pupils was Niklas Zennström. He was born in 1966 and grew up in a family where most members chose careers like teaching, art or writing. Niklas' interest in programming and his admiration for entrepreneurs like Steve Jobs and Bill Gates led him to pursue studies in engineering physics and computer science at Uppsala University. His capacity for hard work enabled him to obtain a dual degree in both subjects. After eight years working for a company owned by the entrepreneur Jan Stenbeck, he was ready to spread his wings. The tech sector was booming, and optimism was running high. Online business opportunities seemed limitless, and the Stockholm share index had risen by 80 per cent in just five months.

But then came the dot-com crash on 6 March 2000. Stock markets tumbled, and when the NASDAQ index lost 24 per cent of its value in April, many IT firms went bankrupt. Within a year, the Stockholm exchange lost a third of its value. It affected the entire economy. The crash was the largest in Swedish history.

Not the ideal time to start up a new tech company, then. But Niklas Zennström had an unshakeable belief in the project he had launched with his Danish business partner Janus Friis. Within a few months they had launched Kazaa, based on a file-sharing protocol developed by the Estonian programmers Ahti Heinla, Priit Kasesalu and Jaan Tallinn. Kazaa rapidly became the world's most-downloaded program, with over 200 million users. It was based on the *peer-to-peer* (P2P) principle, meaning that all Kazaa users were connected to a single vast computer network. Problems arose, though, when the service was also used for illegal music downloading. That prompted the music industry to sue the company.

Then Zennström and Friis reasoned, if all those users were connected via the internet, they ought to be able to phone each other via the net. That was the start of IP telephony. The project was initially called 'Sky Peer-to-Peer', which was soon shortened to 'Skyper'. Because the domain for Skyper was already taken, they changed the name again to 'Skype'. For many years, Skype was the leading IP telephony service, with over 300 million users. The company was acquired by eBay in 2005. Since 2011, Skype has been owned by Microsoft.

The business model was based on a basic service that was free. At the same time, users were enticed to pay for services such as 'Skype Out', which made it possible to make global calls at local rates, and 'Skype In', which was a subscription to a local phone number regardless of where you were in the world.

During the coronavirus pandemic, Skype was used by 40 million people a day, including for work meetings. Skype was first on the scene followed by competitors like Zoom, Google Meet and Microsoft Teams.

Niklas Zennström has also made marks in other ways. He is a multi-billionaire and runs Atomico, a venture capital firm that invests in companies that generate solutions for the climate and environment. He also supports many initiatives and promising new innovators via his Zennström Philanthropies foundation.

The map of life

THE HUMAN PROTEIN ATLAS

An atlas enables us to travel in our imagination, find out about places we'd like to visit and – most importantly – obtain a bird's-eye perspective over a large area. The human body consists of more than 20,000 different proteins. They are now mapped in the Human Protein Atlas, a huge database that is freely accessible online.

After the human genome was fully mapped in 2003, many scientists turned their attention to the body's proteins. And to Sweden, because this is where scientists were setting up the Human Protein Atlas (HPA), which has been called the world's most complex research project ever undertaken. Dr Mathias Uhlén, professor of microbiology at KTH Royal Institute of Technology, has been in charge of the ever-expanding project right from the start. His 750 scientific publications underline his status as a leading researcher, while his 80 patents show that he is a successful innovator. The Human Protein Atlas is by far the most ambitious innovation he has spearheaded, with contributions from scientists and physicians all over the world. Collectively, their input is equivalent to more than 1,500 person-years.

The project has focused on cataloguing information about all the proteins in the human body. Every gene in the DNA molecule represents a recipe for a particular protein, which means that more than 20,000 different proteins interact in intricate ways in our bodies. Proteins are always involved in illness. For example, if our pancreas stops producing the protein insulin, we will develop diabetes. If the protein beta-amyloid forms clumps that obstruct nerve signals, we will develop Alzheimer's disease. That's why 99 per cent of all medicines act on proteins in some way. And that's why the Human Protein Atlas is such a key resource.

In order to map the proteins in our cells, scientists had to start by generating particular types of proteins called antibodies. Each antibody marks the presence of a certain protein, so there are more than 20,000 different types. Without antibodies to start with, researchers would be like anglers fishing without a hook. The antibodies generated in Stockholm were sent to pathologists at labs linked to the project. The pathologists tested the antibodies in a number of human tissue samples from organs such as the lung, kidney and brain. Then the project team in

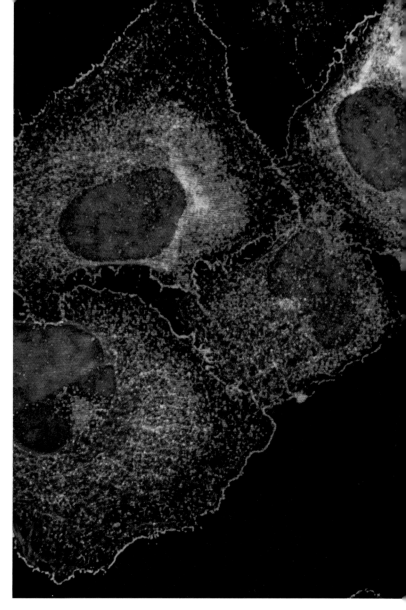

Stockholm created high-resolution digital images and annotated them to show the presence of each protein and its expression.

Most proteins are present in all cells, but some are specific to particular tissues. That means that doctors and scientists all over the world can compare their tissue samples from patients' tumour biopsies with the images in the Human Protein Atlas. This enables them to determine which proteins are involved in a patient's tumour and thus make a more precise diagnosis. New images are being added to the Atlas all the time. Today, this reference database contains more than 13 million high-resolution images.

The Human Protein Atlas is also a crucial resource for researchers working in labs in many different countries to come up with more-targeted pharmaceuticals. New medicines take time to develop, with a significant testing phase required before they can be put on the market. The Human Protein Atlas is an incredibly powerful tool for individual doctors and pharmaceutical companies alike. The open-access Atlas has around four million online visitors each year, making it one of the world's most-visited biological databases. The main funding source for the project is a grant from the Knut and Alice Wallenberg Foundation, one of the largest grants ever awarded in Sweden.

For Mathias Uhlén, the project has been an opportunity to get close to the magic of life – on the cellular level. While he is hopeful for the future, he is also careful to point out the limits of the Human Protein Atlas, saying: 'We are producing a map of the terrain, but that's not the only thing you need if you want to find treasures or avoid hazards.'

The Human Protein Atlas contains over 13 million highresolution images that anyone can freely use. This image represents human cells, where the cell nucleus is blue and the green and red colours indicate different proteins in the cell.

A totally new deliverance

SPOTIFY

At the start of the 21st century, the music industry was in freefall. Collapsing record sales and a Wild West of pirate copying and illegal downloading meant record companies were on the verge of going under. But a rare combination of clever ideas and hard work from a group centred around two young Swedes transformed music distribution for ever.

Daniel Ek and Martin Lorentzon had both achieved success as entrepreneurs in the 1990s IT boom and earned big money from on-line advertising. When the dot-com bubble burst, the friends pondered what to do next.

The music industry was going through a tough time. Record companies' revenues sank as CDs, viewed as overpriced, were losing market share. Meanwhile, more and more people were downloading music illegally. File-sharing was hard to stop. Political debates pitted creators' intellectual property rights against consumers' rights of free access to knowledge and culture. While the debate raged, music industry revenues halved.

Ek and Lorentzon started sketching out a completely new music distribution model. Instead of owning music, consumers would 'borrow' it, a bit like library books – but digitally. The two men spent two years visiting music production companies and presenting their concept of a free, advertising-funded streaming service that would pay production companies and musicians a certain sum per listen. No investors were willing to commit before any licensing agreements had been signed. But offering employee stock options – essentially a promise of a share in the company's future profits – helped them to attract some of Sweden's best computer programmers.

Streaming services deliver the music while you listen, with no need to download files from the internet. The technology required the cream of programming talent. One such figure was Ludvig Strigeus, a software engineer and graduate of Chalmers University of Technology in Gothenburg. Strigeus created a new concept for the rapid online transfer of music files by chopping them up into small pieces before transferring them. The technology was refined further by Andreas Ehn, another Spotify pioneer. They had to struggle with a knotty problem

that occurred after the files were transferred. In order to play a song, the pieces of the song file had to be reunited and reassembled in the right order. Ehn hit upon the solution of slicing the music files lengthwise instead of vertically. As these long, thin strips were transferred, the program could start with any one of them and essentially start playing the track straight away. The software didn't need to pick up the various parts in any particular order, so transfer speeds increased dramatically.

Spotify launched in April 2006. The international record companies Spotify partnered with had stipulated that an ad-free monthly paid subscription service should be offered in addition to the ad-supported 'freemium' model. Users would sign up with an account to use the software. Spotify was available only to specially selected testers in a beta version until October 2008. As lessons learned from those early adopters were taken on board, the service was gradually opened up to more users.

Spotify for iPhone and Android was launched in the early hours of 7 September 2009. Suddenly, all you needed was a smartphone to access nearly all the music in the world. And if you'd received an invitation from a previous user, it was completely free.

This sense of exclusivity helped Spotify's rapid expansion in music circles. In March 2011, the service reached one million paying customers. A few months later, Napster's founder Sean Parker helped to launch the service in the United States. Spotify signed a deal with Mark Zuckerberg to enable Spotify users to access their tracks and playlists in Facebook.

The service has continued to expand and improve over the following years, with algorithms ensuring each user's recommended tracks are tailored to their preferences, options to create special playlists for different activities with different styles and tempos, a sensor that detects the user's movements and adapts the playlist to their speed – and more.

Spotify's expansion into offering podcasts and audiobooks also had knock-on effects on related industries. Today, the service has several competitors, and the field is adjusting along with customers' changing preferences and rapid advances in technology.

Of course, there are critical voices from some quarters concerning what is now the world's largest music service, including creators of niche music who feel under-represented and some established artists who say the payments are too low. But one thing is clear: Spotify has not just saved parts of the music industry from ruin. It has also done a lot to democratise access to music. Record company bosses' power is no longer absolute. Anyone can upload their music to Spotify. In effect, this means every user has access to 40,000 new songs – every single day.

Martin Lorentzon, one of Spotify's founders, explains the company's timeline in the foyer of its Stockholm head office. Today, Spotify has around 400 million users worldwide.

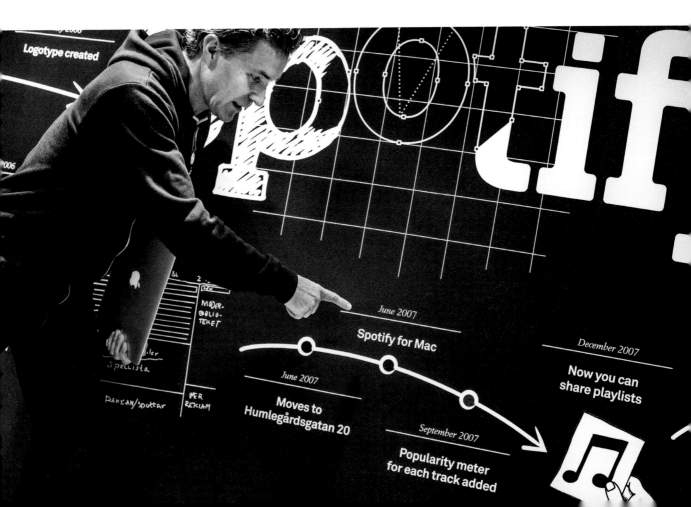

Seeing the invisible

THE VISUALIZATION TABLE

Sometimes an image is more useful than reality. Doctors and medical students can lean over and rotate, zoom in, tap and study an image with their fingertips – the same way as on a small phone screen. It's easy to forget that the three-dimensional image of a human body being displayed is not the real thing.

It's about mathematics and data science. Transforming vast quantities of data into meaningful graphics. The subject has long interested Anders Ynnerman, professor of science visualisation at Linköping University and director of Norrköping Visualization Center C. The 3D visualisation technology his research team developed in the mid-2000s has enabled advances in medical applications for research and education, and provided a tool for science communication and education at museums and science centres.

Before you can visualise anything, you need to obtain data. For example, the data might come from computer tomography, which can create an image of the inside of the human body. This is where Anders Persson, another pioneer, physician and scientist, enters the picture. He is an expert in medical imaging science and visualisation. Like Anders Ynnerman, he is also passionate about finding practical uses for research.

The idea for the Visualization Table emerged as Visualization Center C was being set up. Unlike typical science centres, the concept for Visualization Center C was based on the power of visual images and ways of interacting with digital graphics to learn more about outer space, the human body, historical events and any other fields involving processes, changes, or 'before and after'. The centre was opened in 2010. It is a joint project involving Linköping University, the municipality of Norrköping and RISE Interactive C-studio, headed by Thomas Rydell – another key figure who saw the potential of 3D technology early on.

In parallel with their involvement with Visualization Center C, the Linköping researchers set their sights on the medical market. They teamed up with Sectra, a medical IT company, to license their innovation. In 2011, Linköping University became the first institution in the world to use this brand-new digital tool in its teaching.

Following pages: The Visualization Table is used in medical schools all over the world, as well as in museums and science centres.

With the creators' revolutionary software, users can create a virtual three-dimensional copy of the body, which they can then turn and rotate and even slice into layers to examine various organs. This is an amazing teaching and learning tool for physicians and medical students. As a virtual model where doctors can try out their interventions before applying them on human patients, it helps physicians provide more precisely targeted treatment. Medical professionals have benefitted from studying coronary circulation in detail. New visualisation technology enables them to observe how blood circulates through the atria and ventricles, as well as heart muscle contractions and any leaks.

But the technology works with more than living bodies. It also enables non-invasive, highly detailed examination of the bodies of people who have died as a result of illness, accidents or crimes in order to establish the exact cause of death. In some cases, when religious beliefs preclude a regular autopsy, the virtual autopsy table has provided a solution.

Even long-dead bodies can be examined, with mummies providing the most striking examples. This innovation was used in 2013 to take a closer look at the Gebelein Man, a mummy in the British Museum. The analysis of his remains enabled researchers to establish that the man, who lived some 5,500 years ago, had been murdered. Someone had stabbed him in the back with a sharp implement. After studying similar injuries in recent murder cases, Anders Persson concluded that the attack had slashed through Gebelein Man's pulmonary artery and punctured his lung.

Museum visitors can study a digital copy of a mummy using a Visualization Table located next to the physical mummy. Work on visualising the Gebelein Man mummy led to the establishment of Interspectral as a spin-off company from Visualization Center C in 2014 with Thomas Rydell as the first CEO. Interspectral has developed public 3D visualisation displays into a new Swedish export product. Now millions of children and young people all over the world can explore scientific mysteries in a way that really engages their curiosity.

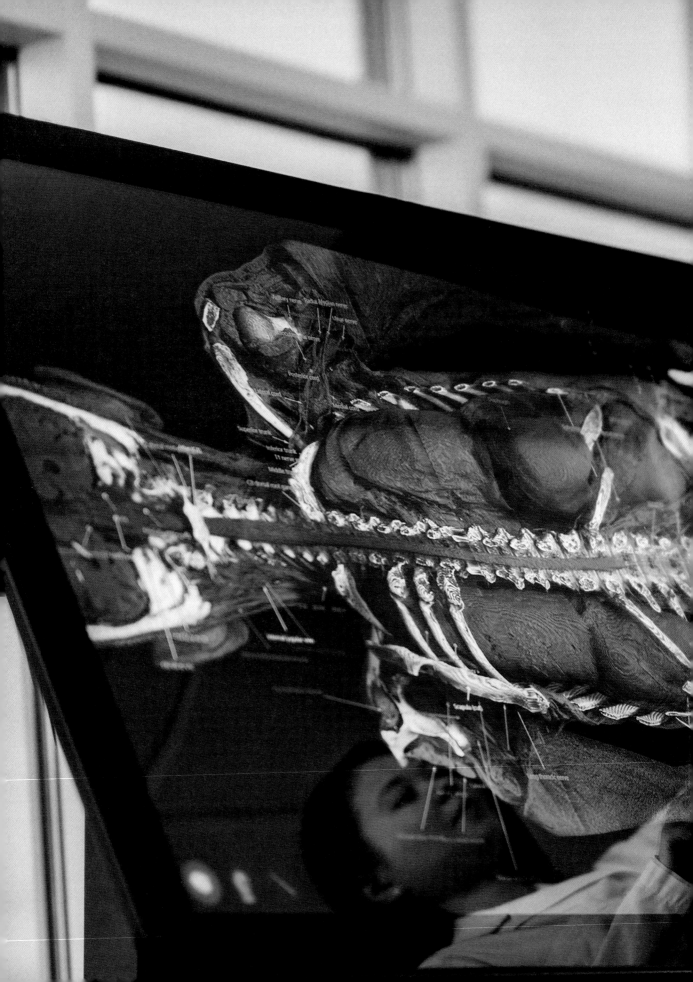

Clean water from the sun

SOLVATTEN

Two billion people – nearly 30 per cent of the Earth's population – lack access to clean water at home. Solvatten, which means 'solar water' in Swedish, is the brand name for a clever black container. People pour dirty water into it, and clean water comes out. As the name indicates, the container uses solar energy to purify the water, destroying microbiological contamination, such as parasites and bacteria.

The traditional way to purify water is by boiling. It has traditionally been considered women's work. Often, children are expected to help with the time-consuming task of gathering firewood and kindling. Wood fires release carbon dioxide into the atmosphere and generate soot and smoke in homes, which are harmful to health. Burning wood also leads to deforestation, loss of biodiversity and soil erosion, because tree roots are needed to keep the soil stable. Research has shown that up to 70 per cent of all energy consumed in sub-Saharan Africa is used for boiling water.

In the late 1990s, Petra Wadström, a designer and artist and former research assistant, was living in Australia with her family. She also travelled around Indonesia and visited several developing countries in Africa. She was distressed to see how many people in those areas lacked access to clean water and suffered health problems as a result, but she was also determined to do something about the problem. The contrast between the overabundance of sunlight and the lack of clean water at those latitudes stuck in her mind.

Wadström was convinced the solution had to be small-scale and accessible for people in their daily lives. In order to work, it had to be extremely durable, with no expensive filters or other parts that needed to be replaced. And even more crucially, it had to be easy to use. She had seen too many examples of projects where people from wealthy countries told impoverished families how they should live their lives. Petra Wadström realised that if her idea was going to work, its design and marketing would need to show an understanding of and respect for the circumstances in which people would use it in their day-to-day lives.

Petra Wadström produced some prototypes and sure enough, UV rays and warmth from the sun destroyed microorganisms' DNA,

Solvatten systems use the sun's rays to purify and heat water, destroying harmful microorganisms. It saves time, especially for women and children. For Priscilla Lokisiau, a teacher from western Kenya, a Solvatten container also serves as a conversation starter for her pupils to discuss science and social issues.

preventing them from multiplying. The sun both purified and heated the water. She gave an early version to families in Nepal, Thailand, Indonesia and South Africa to try it out. The users provided valuable feedback, which led to further improvements. In 2011, production of Solvatten containers started in earnest, and so did cooperation with the companies and organisations that finance Solvatten as part of their sustainability work. Keeping this collaboration going is as important a key to success as the production itself. Today, Solvatten is used by more than 500,000 people in over 40 countries.

One of those countries is Uganda, which has poorly developed infrastructure and has taken in more than 1.4 million refugees fleeing conflict in other nearby countries. The situation has led to catastrophic environmental and living conditions, while energy, water and food shortages cause further tension and conflicts between local communities and refugee families. Diseases such as typhus, cholera and dysentery, all of which cause severe diarrhoea, spread easily and lead to malnutrition, particularly among children. Since 2020, PLAN International and UNHCR have been working to roll out Solvatten units in these areas to deal with water issues and increase the use of solar energy outside Uganda's electricity grid.

Petra Wadström has received numerous awards and commendations for her invention, which saves lives every day. She is also proud of the fact that it frees up time for women. That's time they can use to help their children with their schoolwork, improve their own skills or just to rest. Wadström says she has not just invented a device to purify water; she has also created freedom – more freedom for women.

The space shower

ORBITAL SYSTEMS

We may live on the 'blue planet', but fresh water is in short supply. Just 1 per cent of all the water on Earth is suitable for drinking. And most of the water we use goes down the plughole – even though it's clean. Fortunately, circular systems allow most fresh water to be saved and reused.

Mehrdad Mahdjoubi studied industrial design at Lund University, where he was involved in a joint project with NASA. How might people shower on Mars? Project participants learned everything there was to know about water recycling and purification in a closed system. They also investigated what kinds of processors, high-tech filters and valves would be needed for user-friendly, reliable operation of a shower. Mahdjoubi took those ideas further. Wouldn't they be worth putting into practice here on Earth too?

Circular systems are a must in outer space, but they are just as necessary for us here on Earth. The Orbital Shower uses up to 90 per cent less water than ordinary showers.

A 10-minute shower uses around 100 litres of hot water, most of which drains away. But the shower constructed by Mehrdad Mahdjoubi reduces that consumption by up to 90 per cent. It also results in energy savings of around 80 per cent.

This is achieved by means of sensors that analyse the shower water 20 times per second. Water that is too dirty is directed down the drain; the rest is recirculated. The system filters, purifies and reheats the water, and an integrated heat pump maintains water pressure and flow. It also means that the water is at the right temperature right away – which also implies less waste. Homeowners who install a smart shower with this advanced technology can also monitor their water and energy savings via an app.

Mehrdad Mahdjoubi founded Orbital Systems in 2012, when he was still living in his student digs in Lund. Ten years later, his company employs 70 people, with headquarters in Malmö's old Riksbank building and production in the historic former Facit adding machine factory in the town of Åtvidaberg. A new chapter of Swedish industrial history is now being written. Buoyed by US$20 million in venture capital, the company is optimistic. Investors include prominent names like Niklas Zennström, of Skype fame, and Amazon's Jeff Bezos.

The next challenge Orbital Systems is going to tackle is the toilet. Mahdjoubi has long been annoyed that we use perfectly clean drinking water to flush our toilets. He plans to use his new funding to develop a solution that reuses water from the bathroom sink in the toilet.

Discussions about water use have typically focused almost exclusively on supply. Mehrdad Mahdjoubi believes that by turning our attention to efficient, circular solutions, we can reduce demand and thus conserve the Earth's precious, limited resources.

A protective collar

HÖVDING HEAD PROTECTION

The risk of head injuries for cyclists involved in accidents has been known since the late 19th century, when safety-minded people donned pith helmets to take a spin on their velocipedes. That was not an option for racing cyclists, though. They needed more aerodynamic, effective protection to prevent head injuries in high-speed crashes. For many years, helmet use was mainly confined to cycling sports, but then in the 1970s the first fibreglass helmets appeared on the market.

Bike helmets are ugly, cumbersome to wear – and they wreck your hairstyle. Besides, some people say, they encourage cyclists to ride carelessly. In that case, it is better to pay attention to the risks and ride cautiously. However, the obvious risk of head injury led to a new Swedish regulation in 2005, requiring children aged under 15 to wear a bicycle helmet. Children aren't the only ones at risk of serious injury in cycle accidents, though. Wouldn't the next logical step have been to introduce a universal cycle helmet requirement?

While around half of Swedes were in favour of compulsory helmets for children, surveys showed that only around 9 per cent of adults wore a helmet. That's why Anna Haupt and Terese Alstin, two young industrial design students at Lund University, wondered whether there might be another way to protect cyclists' skulls besides the unfashionable, bulky cycle helmet.

Inspired by the automotive industry's airbags, Haupt and Alstin created an 'invisible' helmet that a cyclist could wear inside a collar round their neck. The invention is based on sensors that trigger a helmet-shaped airbag to inflate around the person's head in 100 milliseconds when they register the sort of abnormal body movements that occur in a cycle accident. The airbag inflates with an explosive burst that is guaranteed to attract the attention of bystanders. To the cyclist, it feels like a couple of giant hands taking hold of their head, but they are well protected inside the white balloon-like hood. Like other modern Swedish inventions, such as the seat belt and the baby carrier, it combines freedom with protection by enabling people to get around more safely.

A year after submitting their thesis project, Haupt and Alstin founded a company called Hövding to develop their idea. A produc-

Inspired by car airbags, Anna Haupt and Terese Alstin designed an 'invisible' bike helmet that fits around the wearer's neck like a collar. The technology is based on sensors that detect abnormal body movements just before a cycle crash.

tion model of the airbag helmet was launched on the market in 2012. It provides a high level of protection in many accident scenarios.

Today, around 500,000 head protections have been sold to people in 15 countries.

Investments for good

GREEN BONDS

Pension funds account for a large chunk of overall global stock market value, and they are influential institutional investors. Meanwhile, more and more pension savers are looking for environmentally responsible investments. They now have a new option, known as green bonds.

Green bonds are an economic innovation – economic in the sense of supply and demand, as well as the 'thrifty' sense of being economical with natural resources. These investment instruments are about matching new, environmentally responsible, climate-friendly projects with investors looking to benefit the environment while growing their capital. In 2020, the total value of green bonds passed the milestone of US$1 trillion, and they continue to attract new investors. Nearly a third of EU stimulus packages issued during the coronavirus pandemic in 2020 were financed through green bonds – originally a Swedish innovation.

A bond is somewhat similar to a loan. A party planning to launch a project or long-term business venture can offer bonds to investors. Unlike a loan, which can only be issued by a bank or other credit institution, a bond offers a way for institutions such as pension funds or insurance companies to invest directly in various projects. In general, bonds are less risky investments than shares – though they are not risk-free.

Green bonds were the brainchild of Christopher Flensborg, Head of Climate and Sustainable Finance at Swedish bank SEB, in 2007. The idea was sparked by demand from a number of funds and insurance companies seeking to invest in promising green ventures. They were looking for a reliable, creditworthy intermediary. SEB got the World Bank on board to help develop the concept. They made a good team, though their timing could have been better. Just when the first green bond was about to be launched in 2008, the collapse of Lehman Brothers in New York triggered a global financial crisis.

In 2013, the world's first green corporate bond was issued by Vasakronan, a Swedish property company, to fund construction projects with market-leading environmental certification requirements. The city of Gothenburg was another early issuer. It issued a green bond

The Lackarebäck water treatment plant near Gothenburg boasts the largest ultrafilter facility in the Nordic countries, financed by green bonds. An ultra filter works by passing water through a system of 30,000 kilometres of spaghetti-thin pipes, removing even bacteria and viruses.

to finance an upgrade of its municipal water treatment facilities. In global terms, the energy and transport sectors have seen the largest investments, while projects to support biodiversity and establish wetlands have also benefitted.

The green bond market has experienced explosive growth. Today, there are also products for individual investors. Because 'green bond' is not a protected name – that is, it is not a trademarked brand – the term has spread all over the world. Now many bonds with green features are issued outside the framework drawn up by SEB and the World Bank.

There is no doubt that green bonds have positive impacts. The key to the success of the concept is not just down to the huge demand for environmental projects. It also shows the crucial role played by a competent intermediary between investors and project owners. Issuing a green bond requires immense financial and technical knowledge, but social and ethical aspects also require due consideration. Careful scrutiny is key, and SEB has benefitted greatly from its cooperation with the World Bank, which has many years' experience dealing with charitable organisations and NGOs around the globe.

The consensus is that reducing emissions is the only sustainable long-term climate option. New investment solutions are needed to enable investment in new technologies – and to help companies transform their business models.

Instead of plastic

PAPIRA

Fragile products need protective packaging. For decades, moulded plastic derived from petroleum has been used for that purpose. Now a fossil-free alternative is available: Papira is a lightweight cushioning foam material made from wood cellulose – and it's biodegradable.

Traditional plastic foams have many drawbacks. Polyethylene (PE) foam and expanded polystyrene (EPS), also called Styrofoam, are made from petroleum, a fossil-based material. They contribute to global warming when they are incinerated after use. If plastic does not end up in a waste incinerator, it causes other environmental problems. Tiny particles known as microplastics can enter waterways and reach beaches and oceans, where fish consume the plastic particles, mistaking them for food, and die of starvation.

When Åsa Ek, a research engineer, was recruited to join a start-up called Cellutech, she arrived with a degree in polymer chemistry from Stockholm's KTH Royal Institute of Technology, and nearly a decade of R&D experience in the biomedical industry. The team she joined was developing innovative wood-based products based on groundbreaking research conducted at the Wallenberg Wood Science Center, a research institute founded to bring academia and industry together in the search for innovations. One material that was generating a lot of interest was nanocellulose, a completely nature-based material with the potential to replace petroleum-based plastics.

Obtained from wood, nanocellulose consists of extremely fine, strong fibres. The material was first studied in the 1980s, but it was difficult and expensive to obtain. Then scientists at KTH developed a new, cost-effective technique. They attracted a great deal of interest when they managed to spin the ultrafine fibres into threads that were stiffer and stronger than spider silk – the strongest naturally occurring thread. One of the research teams started experimenting with bubbles and foam made from nanocellulose. That work was spearheaded by Lars Wågberg, professor of fibre technology at KTH.

Figuring out how to make the surfaces of the bubbles in the foam sufficiently stable to resist collapse after drying was a challenge, even for a foam scientist. We all know what happens with soap suds in the kitchen sink – when the suds dry, the bubbles disappear. In 2012, Lars Wågberg's research team managed to get nanocellulose bubbles to dry and form a firm, stable foam at room temperature. This breakthrough led to three new patents, and the foam material underwent further development at Cellutech, now with Åsa Ek as the company's CEO.

But for Ek and her colleagues, nanocellulose was just one step along the way. They sought out areas where such a lightweight, recyclable cushioning material would come into its own. Could it be used in medical applications? As insulation or in packaging? While that market analysis was underway, the company also studied ways to scale up production. That's where they ran into a problem. In order to produce a firm, dry foam, 98–99 per cent of the moisture had to be removed from the nanofibres. It was fairly easy to dry small batches of foam in

Papira, a new cushioning material, is entirely wood-based and fully recyclable along with paper packaging.

the lab, but in larger quantities the material became harder to manage. Åsa Ek and her colleagues realised how expensive production would be. Was this the end of the road?

They refused to give up and started exploring new avenues. Discussions with possible future customers alerted them to the potential for a fossil-free, cushioning packing material. Did it have to be based on nanocellulose? Or could they make another material with similar properties from ordinary pulp?

Soon they managed to create a hard foam from conventional cellulose fibres with the cushioning properties the market needed. This new material was named Papira.

Stora Enso, a major paper and packaging manufacturer, had showed interest early on by acquiring a share in Cellutech. It was a fruitful relationship. In October 2018, Stora Enso became sole owner of Cellutech, with Åsa Ek becoming head of the bioinnovation division. The coronavirus pandemic broke out just as Stora Enso was setting up a pilot production facility for Papira at its Fors plant in northern Sweden. Online retailing experienced a major boost. Today, more than two billion people shop online – that's more than one in four people around the world buying everything from clothes to sensitive electronics and fragile porcelain items. Stora Enso has fielded hundreds of enquiries from clients in various sectors interested in testing Papira packing materials to protect their goods in transit.

Stora Enso aims to establish Papira as the new standard in protective packaging. Many more items derived from wood products are currently in development. Scientists are convinced that any materials made from petroleum can also be made from wood. All it takes is innovation.

Fully 70 per cent of Sweden's land is covered in forest, which generates renewable materials used in many products – including Papira.

Afterword

INNOVATION AND COLLABORATION

This book showcases many different facets of innovation. All of the stories feature fundamentally human motivations: problem-solving, creativity and striving for improvement. We have gained insights into fascinating personal stories that demonstrate the tenacity, talent and imagination it takes to achieve success. As the timeline approached the present day, the tales of isolated geniuses became rarer, supplanted by team efforts involving companies and universities.

The roots of many of these innovations stretch far back in history. We are now living in the future those innovators dreamed of. They worked hard, often to their very limits, not just for their own sake but for ours as well. Sweden has benefitted from a fortunate combination of circumstances that helped make us one of the world's most innovative nations. Free universal education and a stable social welfare system, along with a number of other factors, have stimulated people's curiosity and zeal for problem-solving.

The challenges facing humankind today differ in many respects from those in Alfred Nobel's or Jonas Wenström's day. In addition to ongoing global crises like climate change, water scarcity and biodiversity loss, we now have to reckon with the war and energy crisis in Europe, with rampant inflation and higher food prices as consequences. Not a situation anyone would have wished for when the world is just emerging from a pandemic and all the associated personal suffering and considerable costs to society.

We share those current crises and future challenges with the rest of the world. Our creativity and ability to work together will be put to the test. But without innovation, we won't get carbon dioxide emissions down or solve the energy crisis. Innovative work will require close collaboration across national borders. European cooperation is of crucial importance, and Sweden has a great deal to contribute.

Apart from our successes, there are also areas where we can learn from one another. Sweden has a lot of start-up companies, but relatively few that are capable of scaling up their operations for growth. That's something larger countries are better at. The European common market is important for all of us here.

Sweden has long relied on its highly educated population in combination with world-leading research and advanced IT infrastructure as trump cards, but that might not be sufficient any longer. Businesses both large and small are worried about poor educational attainment in schools and new staff recruitment for tech jobs – concerns Sweden shares with other European countries. Similarly, storm clouds are gathering around the use of technology. After decades of solid progress, Sweden is now starting to lag behind in international rankings. Businesses of all sizes are suffering from a lack of skilled, tech-savvy workers, particularly in IT. This is an area where we could benefit from others' experience. Sweden's digital infrastructure needs to expand even further.

Despite Sweden's ambitious goals for equality and diversity, few innovations are helmed by women, and less than 10 per cent of patents are issued to women. The majority of innovations are attributed to men, and men control a whopping 99 per cent of venture capital.

Solutions to many of these challenges lie in closer European cooperation in matters surrounding innovation. Our European neighbours have many of the same constellations of problems, and we share similar hopes for the opportunities that innovation offers. We all agree that innovation drives economic growth. But views differ about what it takes to stimulate innovation. Money plays a crucial role, but so do recognition and political commitment. A favourable climate for innovation emerges from a complex interplay between academia, business, politics and culture. If those elements are in place, new ideas can come about from individuals as well as collaborative endeavours.

Many of the innovations in this book came about before people were aware of global warming or understood the importance of flourishing ecosystems in the seas and on land. Going forward, innovations will have to address many problems all at once.

Some companies have already adapted their production processes and their business models. Even so, change is happening too slowly. Laws and regulations are not keeping pace. Legacy systems and structures also slow things down. We need more business leaders willing to take risks and drive change towards more sustainable, circular business models. Here, too, European cross-border cooperation offers a natural platform.

There are new opportunities all the time. For example, an ambitious venture in northern Sweden aims to slash carbon dioxide emissions from steel production. Three state-owned enterprises – SSAB, a steel manufacturer; LKAB, a mining company; and Vattenfall, a power company – have joined forces in the Hybrit partnership to produce fossil-free steel. Scientists from KTH Royal Institute of Technology are integral to the project, and a pilot plant has been built in Luleå. Their innovative method, which uses hydrogen gas instead of coal and coke to reduce iron ore into iron, has been proved to work. SSAB produced its first sample batch of steel using the Hybrit process in July 2021. The project has attracted interest from around the world. Its first customer was Volvo.

Another start-up, H2 Green Steel, plans to manufacture fossil-free steel at a new facility near Boden in Sweden's far north. That plant will also use hydrogen gas to produce iron ore, which will then be smelted in electric arc furnaces.

In Skellefteå, Northvolt has built Europe's largest battery factory, where it will manufacture lithium-ion batteries for electric vehicles and energy storage.

These processes consume vast amounts of energy, and the need for green electricity is a clear example of a driving force behind innovation in today's world. We need to expand renewable energy sources and improve storage facilities in order to utilise solar, wind and hydroelectric energy. At the same time, other applications are also seeing greater demand for electricity, such as electric vehicle charging. Meanwhile, geopolitical tensions are running higher than any time in the last half-century, so good relations in Europe are vital.

Along with the green transition and digital technologies, materials science is an area that is transforming everything from electronics to pharmaceuticals. Nanotechnology is not so much a distinct field as a new toolbox for all the techniques we can now start to use to manipulate the innermost components of materials. Nanotechnology enables transformative innovations that might seem like science fiction to many laypeople.

Innovations need to be tested. It was true for Anders Celsius, and it's still true today. One major difference is that testing facilities are becoming increasingly high-tech – and pricey. Great hopes are being placed in the European Spallation Source (ESS) and MAX IV, two new multi-disciplinary research facilities located near Lund in southern Sweden. Both installations can be likened to enormous microscopes. When the ESS is ready for operation in 2027, it will be the most powerful neutron source in the world. MAX IV offers researchers access to more powerful X-ray beams than any other facility. It is already up and running, with plans to serve thousands of scientists every year.

Back in 1675, Sir Isaac Newton coined the metaphor 'standing on the shoulders of giants' to describe the way innovations almost always build on the work of earlier researchers. Now, though, innovations no longer rest on the shoulders of a few individual giants; they rely on a vast global network. This is particularly clear in the life sciences.

The numerous medical and pharmaceutical innovations in this book are a reflection of Sweden's strength in this broad, deep field. Sweden drew up a national life-science strategy in 2019, and today many of the nation's resources are concentrated around the concept of 'precision health'. As a result, medical diagnoses are more precise, and subsequent treatment can be tailored to each patient. Combining data on individual's biology, lifestyle and environment with epidemiological studies and other public health data generates better information for all sorts of decision-makers. We now know, for example, that air pollution and sedentary lifestyles are major risk factors for strokes, and that knowledge can feed into urban planning.

Freedom of thought is crucial for innovation. A stable democracy is fundamental to science and progress. History shows that beneficial innovations do not come about under dictatorships. Perhaps that is the single most important factor for a Europe that is to remain strong and free – *innovation the European way*.

The vision statement of the Royal Swedish Academy of Engineering Sciences is 'technology in the service of humanity'. We believe that skills in technology, economics and related scientific fields contribute to the improvement of people's lives. By focusing on the right things and investing wisely, I am convinced that we will see further innovations prior generations couldn't have dreamed of.

Tuula Teeri
President, the Royal Swedish Academy of Engineering Sciences (IVA)

Index

Image credits

About the authors

Henrik Berggren is a journalist and writer with a PhD in history. He served as managing editor of the culture section for *Dagens Nyheter*, Sweden's biggest daily paper. Henrik Berggren has received numerous awards and distinctions for his work.

Eva Krutmeijer is a science writer, professional science communicator and leader of collaborative projects involving academia, industry and society – with a special focus on innovation and sustainability.

© Max Ström, 2023
Text: Henrik Berggren and Eva Krutmeijer
Translation from Swedish: Ruth Urbom
Main editor: Jeppe Wikström
Editorial board: Marie Alpman, Ann Brunnberg,
Arne Kaijser, Maria Rankka, Annika Winsth
Cover illustrations: Martin Thelander
Photographs: see image credits page 197
Design: Patric Leo
Image research: Erik G Svensson
Editor: Gabriella Sahlin
Prepress: Italgraf media
Printed by Livonia Print, Latvia, 2023
ISBN: 978-91-7126-592-0
www.maxstrom.se

This book has been published in cooperation
with the Royal Swedish Academy
of Engineering Sciences.